CRE**A**TIVE
HOMEOWNER®

plumbing

step-by-step projects

SMART GUIDE

CREATIVE HOMEOWNER®, Upper Saddle River, New Jersey

Editor: Fran J. Donegan
Photo Researcher: Robyn Poplasky
Editorial Assistants: Jennifer Calvert, Nora Grace
Technical Reviewer: Merle Henkenius, Jim Barrett

Designers: Maureen Mulligan, Annie Jeon
Illustrators: James Randolph, Norman Nuding, Clarke Barre
Cover photography: Merle Henkenius

Creative Homeowner
VP/Editorial Director: Timothy O. Bakke
Production Manager: Kimberly H. Vivas
Art Director: David Geer
Managing Editor: Fran J. Donegan

Current Printing (last digit)
10 9 8 7 6 5 4 3 2 1

Manufactured in the United States of America

Smart Guide: Plumbing
First published as *Quick Guide: Plumbing*
Library of Congress Control Number: 2006934766
ISBN-10: 1-58011-339-7
ISBN-13: 978-1-58011-339-7

CREATIVE HOMEOWNER®
A Division of Federal Marketing Corp.
24 Park Way
Upper Saddle River, NJ 07458
www.creativehomeowner.com

Metric Conversion

Length

1 inch	25.4 mm
1 foot	0.3048 m
1 yard	0.9144 m
1 mile	1.61 km

Area

1 square inch	645 mm²
1 square foot	0.0929 m²
1 square yard	0.8361 m²
1 acre	4046.86 m²
1 square mile	2.59 km²

Volume

1 cubic inch	16.3870 cm³
1 cubic foot	0.03 m³
1 cubic yard	0.77 m³

Common Lumber Equivalents

Sizes: Metric cross sections are so close to their U.S. sizes, as noted below, that for most purposes they may be considered equivalents.

Dimensional lumber	1 x 2	19 x 38 mm
	1 x 4	19 x 89 mm
	2 x 2	38 x 38 mm
	2 x 4	38 x 89 mm
	2 x 6	38 x 140 mm
	2 x 8	38 x 184 mm
	2 x 10	38 x 235 mm
	2 x 12	38 x 286 mm
Sheet sizes	4 x 8 ft.	1200 x 2400 mm
	4 x 10 ft.	1200 x 3000 mm
Sheet thicknesses	¼ in.	6 mm
	⅜ in.	9 mm
	½ in.	12 mm
	¾ in.	19 mm
Stud/joist spacing	16 in. o.c.	400 mm o.c.
	24 in. o.c.	600 mm o.c.

Capacity

1 fluid ounce	29.57 mL
1 pint	473.18 mL
1 quart	1.14 L
1 gallon	3.79 L

Temperature

Celsius = Fahrenheit − 32 x ⅝
Fahrenheit = Celsius x 1.8 + 32

Photo Credits

page 1: courtesy of Kohler **page 2:** *top* Nancy Hill; *all others* Merle Henkenius **page 5:** *top right & bottom* Nancy Hill; *top left* Merle Henkenius **page 8:** Merle Henkenius **page 9:** *top row* Merle Henkenius; *bottom row* www.davidduncanlivingston.com **page 29:** *top left* courtesy of Kohler; *all others* Merle Henkenius **page 39:** *top row* Merle Henkenius; *bottom* courtesy of Ultra Bath **page 51:** *all* Merle Henkenius **page 57:** *all* Merle Henkenius **page 63:** *top left* Freeze Frame Studios/CH; *all others* Merle Henkenius **page 79:** *right* Philip Clayton-Thompson; *bottom left* Merle Henkenius; *top left* Maggie Cole, design: Lauren Muse

contents

safety first

Though all the designs and methods in this book have been reviewed for safety, it is not possible to overstate the importance of using the safest construction methods possible. What follows are reminders; some do's and don'ts of basic carpentry. They are not substitutes for your own common sense.

- *Always* use caution, care, and good judgment when following the procedures described in this book.

- *Always* be sure that the electrical setup is safe; be sure that no circuit is overloaded and that all power tools and electrical outlets are properly grounded. Do not use power tools in wet locations.

- *Always* read container labels on paints, solvents, and other products; provide ventilation, and observe all other warnings.

- *Always* read the manufacturer's instructions for using a tool, especially the warnings.

- *Always* use hold-downs and push sticks whenever possible when working on a table saw. Avoid working short pieces if you can.

- *Always* remove the key from any drill chuck (portable or press) before starting the drill.

- *Always* pay deliberate attention to how a tool works so that you can avoid being injured.

- *Always* know the limitations of your tools. Do not try to force them to do what they were not designed to do.

- *Always* make sure that any adjustment is locked before proceeding. For example, always check the rip fence on a table saw or the bevel adjustment on a portable saw before starting to work.

- *Always* clamp small pieces firmly to a bench or other work surface when using a power tool on them.

- *Always* wear the appropriate rubber or work gloves when handling chemicals, moving or stacking lumber, or doing heavy construction.

- *Always* wear a disposable face mask when you create dust by sawing or sanding. Use a special filtering respirator when working with toxic substances and solvents.

- *Always* wear eye protection, especially when using power tools or striking metal on metal or concrete; a chip can fly off, for example, when chiseling concrete.

- *Always* be aware that there is seldom enough time for your body's reflexes to save you from injury from a power tool in a dangerous situation; everything happens too fast. Be alert!

- *Always* keep your hands away from the business ends of blades, cutters, and bits.

- *Always* hold a circular saw firmly, usually with both hands so that you know where they are.

- *Always* use a drill with an auxiliary handle to control the torque when large-size bits are used.

- *Always* check your local building codes when planning new construction. The codes are intended to protect public safety and should be observed to the letter.

- *Never* work with power tools when you are tired or under the influence of alcohol or drugs.

- *Never* cut tiny pieces of wood or pipe using a power saw. Cut small pieces off larger pieces.

- *Never* change a saw blade or a drill or router bit unless the power cord is unplugged. Do not depend on the switch being off; you might accidentally hit it.

- *Never* work in insufficient lighting.

- *Never* work while wearing loose clothing, hanging hair, open cuffs, or jewelry.

- *Never* work with dull tools. Have them sharpened, or learn how to sharpen them yourself.

- *Never* use a power tool on a workpiece—large or small—that is not firmly supported.

- *Never* saw a workpiece that spans a large distance between horses without close support on each side of the cut; the piece can bend, closing on and jamming the blade, causing saw kickback.

- *Never* support a workpiece from underneath with your leg or other part of your body when sawing.

- *Never* carry sharp or pointed tools, such as utility knives, awls, or chisels, in your pocket. If you want to carry such tools, use a special-purpose tool belt with leather pockets and holders.

plumbing basics

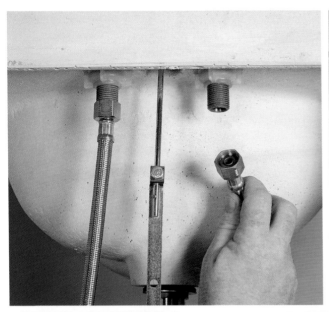

Water Delivery

The illustration on this page shows the parts of a typical home plumbing system via the hot- and cold-water systems. The delivery of potable water is done through pipes or lines that transport it to plumbing fixtures, plumbing appliances, and to outside-the-house spigots. Water enters the home from the municipal or private source through a main pipe, which parcels it into branch lines. Branch lines carry water to fixtures, appliances, and points outside the house.

Plumbing fixtures are sinks (this book uses sink and lavatory interchangeably), toilets, bathtubs, shower stalls, and bidets. Plumbing appliances are washing machines, dishwashers, waste-disposal units, water heaters, and boilers of heating systems. Points outside the house include faucets, in-the-ground lawn sprinklers, and swimming pools.

Every pipe transporting potable water in a modern home plumbing system should have a water shutoff valve, so if it becomes necessary to turn off water on a particular fixture, you will not have to shut down the entire system. The valve on the main pipe, when closed, stops the flow of water throughout the house. It is usually located on the inlet side of the water meter. Shutoff valves on each pipe should be near the fixture or appliance the pipe serves. If an exterior faucet is not equipped with a frost-proof sillcock, there should be a shutoff valve on the inside for the faucet. Turning off water becomes necessary when making a repair.

For example, when a washing machine is not in use, it is a good idea to keep the shutoff valves on the hot- and cold-water branch pipes serving the machine turned off to prevent flooding if a hose connecting a branch pipe to the machine's water-intake valve disintegrates and splits.

If your home is served by a well, a submersible pump and pressure holding tank are parts of the water delivery setup. The top one-third of the tank is filled with air or a sealed rubber bladder that is filled with air. This cushion allows you to draw small quantities of water without triggering the pump. A pressure switch senses the amount of air in the tank. When enough water is drawn off to lower the pressure, the switch turns on the pump.

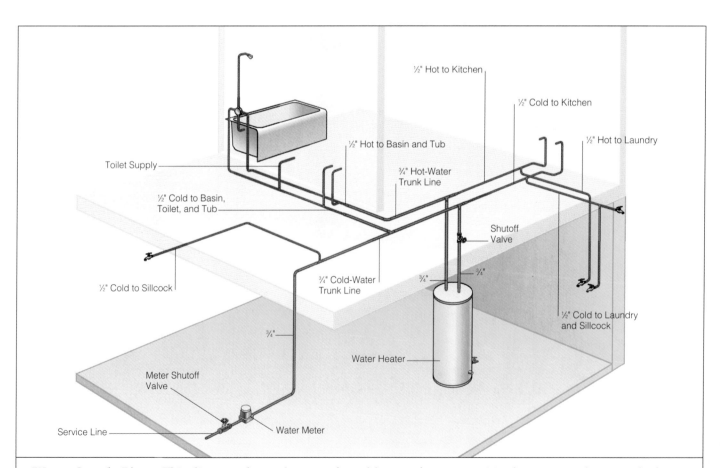

Water Supply Lines. This diagram shows the route for cold water from a municipal water supply to inside the home, and how hot water gets into the water heater and then to fixtures and appliances.

Drainage & Venting

Drainage of waste and sewage is done through a network of various size pipes that transport waste and sewage from fixtures and appliances to the sewer or septic tank/leach field. The largest pipe is the soil pipe. It is the one into which all others drain. The soil pipe transports waste and sewage outside the house to the sewer or septic tank/distribution box network.

Toilets utilize 3-inch, or full-size, drain pipes that are as large as the main soil pipe into which they empty. The water in a toilet bowl serves two purposes: (1) to carry away from the house sewage and waste; (2) to block sewage gas from permeating the house.

Each sink, bathtub, stall shower, bidet, washing machine, and dishwasher is outfitted with the smallest diameter pipes of the drainage network. They are called waste pipes. Each waste pipe has a curved section that remains filled with water. This acts as a trap to block sewer gases. In fact, this section is called a trap.

With a sink, the trap is usually right beneath the sink and in view. With other fixtures and appliances, the trap is exposed below the floor in the basement. If the home does not have a basement, the trap may be embedded in the floor with a removable cover often provided over an opening so there is access to the trap.

The soil pipe and waste pipes of a modern plumbing system should be outfitted with a cleanout plug that can be removed when the pipe becomes clogged.

A typical home has a horizontal soil pipe beneath the basement floor and a full-size vertical stack extending through the roof. Stacks have ½- to 3-inch-diameter branch arms that serve the fixtures on each floor. Larger homes can have several stacks.

Fixtures need to be vented to keep downstream flows from sucking the water from upstream fixture traps. Depleted trap seals allow sewer gas into your home. A short branch arm can use the top half of its pipe as a vent, while longer branches need dedicated vents, called re-vents. Re-vents are also required when a horizontal line steps up in elevation. Two unvented traps, usually the laundry standpipe and floor drain, are allowed under basement floors. All other fixtures must be vented.

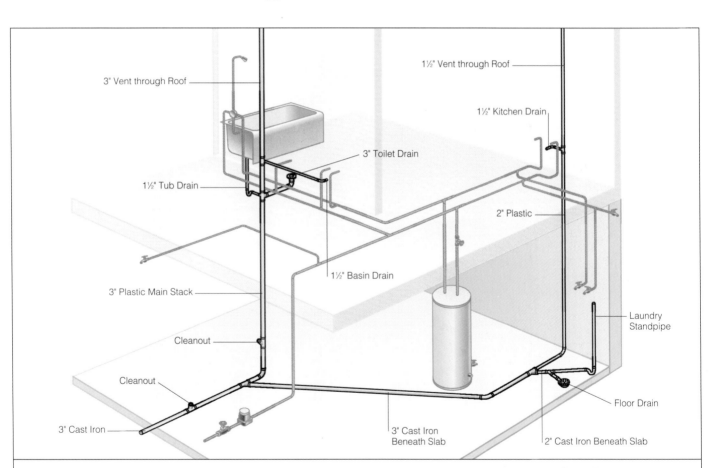

3" Vent through Roof

1½" Vent through Roof

1½" Kitchen Drain

3" Toilet Drain

1½" Tub Drain

2" Plastic

1½" Basin Drain

3" Plastic Main Stack

Cleanout

Laundry Standpipe

Cleanout

Floor Drain

3" Cast Iron

3" Cast Iron Beneath Slab

2" Cast Iron Beneath Slab

Drain and Vent Lines. The drain, waste, vent (DWV) system transports waste and sewage from fixtures and appliances to the sewer or septic tank.

Basic Tools for Plumbing. (A) backsaw, (B) hacksaw, (C) tap, (D) diestock, (E) plunger, (F) Allen wrenches, (G) flat-blade screwdriver, (H) nut driver, (I) Phillips screwdriver, (J) pipe wrench, (K) groove-joint pliers, (L) needle-nose pliers, (M) pliers, (N) chain wrench, (O) multitester, (P) adjustable wrench, (Q) open-end wrench, (R) solder, (S) emery cloth, (T) flux, (U) strap wrench, (V) tubing cutter, (W) tubing bender, (X) basin wrench, (Y) spud wrench

sinks

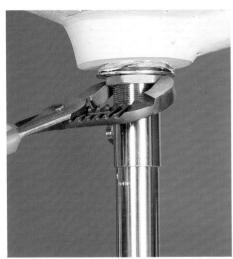
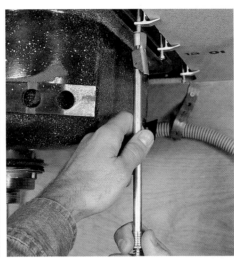
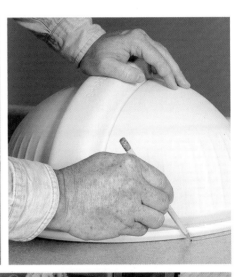

The Anatomy of a Sink

A sink is called a sink unless it is found in a bathroom; then it is called a lavatory. Sink or lavatory, the job it does is the same—to provide a basin to receive potable water, to retain water for as long as you want, and to allow water to drain when you are done with it.

Note: Throughout this section and in this book, the terms "sink" and "lavatory" are often used interchangeably.

Stopping & Straining

They may not look like much, but sinks and lavatories are carefully engineered pieces of equipment. According to most regional codes, sinks and lavatories must have a device to retain water in the basin and to trap matter floating in the water so it cannot flow into the waste pipe, causing a clog. The exception to this is a kitchen sink that supports a food waste-disposal unit. It has a stopper—not a strainer—since you want food scraps to flow down the drain inlet into the disposal.

Most lavatories have pop-up stoppers that are controlled by lift-rods. The height that a stopper can be raised can be limited so any large-size matter will be stopped from flowing through the drain inlet into the waste pipe. Unfortunately, this does not include hair, which tangles around the stem part of the stopper. When enough hair gets entwined, it clogs the drain inlet and restricts the flow. This is the main cause of a lavatory stoppage.

Older lavatories and utility-room sinks use plain rubber or metal stoppers that you insert into and remove from drain inlets by hand. The drain outlets of these lavatories and sinks are outfitted with cross bars that will trap much of the debris floating in the water so it cannot run into the waste pipe.

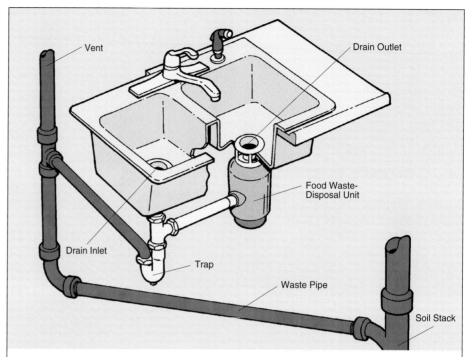

Kitchen Sink. In this double kitchen sink setup equipped with a waste-disposal unit, notice that only one side of the unit has a trap. Most regional plumbing codes permit this if the distance between sink drain openings is 30 in. or less.

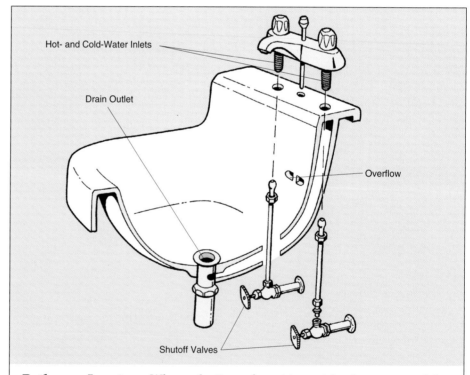

Bathroom Lavatory. When selecting a faucet to match a lavatory or sink, make sure that the hot- and cold-water inlets match the holes in the lavatory or sink.

Drain Outlets

Everyone who has ever used a sink and lavatory knows what a drain outlet looks like. But not everyone realizes that these outlets are drilled to precise measurements. A drain outlet of a kitchen sink is 1½ inches in diameter unless the sink is outfitted with a food waste disposal; then, the mouth of the disposal will be 3½ inches in diameter, but the pipe connection will be 1½ inches. The drain outlet of a sink in a utility room must also be at least 1½ inches in diameter.

The drain outlets of lavatories are drilled so they are at least 1¼ inches in diameter. Although not required by most regional codes, lavatories also may have one or more openings called the overflow. The overflow is located approximately three-quarters of the way up on one wall of the basin. Overflows allow water to drain so it does not flood onto the floor if someone carelessly lets too much of it flow into the lavatory when the stopper is closed or when there is a clog.

The deck holes in sinks and lavs, which are sinks used in bathrooms, vary in number and configuration. Kitchen sinks have long come with three deck holes in an 8-inch spread. A fourth hole, a few inches to the right, allows for a deck-mounted spray nozzle. Lav basins all have three faucet holes in 4- or 8-inch spreads. The wider spread accommodates an undermount faucet, where only the spout and handles are visible. These setups are still standard for kitchen and bathroom sinks, but many of today's solid-surface resin sinks allow other faucet and equipment configurations. The faucet holes for these sinks are usually drilled on site, so you can customize to suit your needs

Surface

You can install a sink or lavatory anywhere, as long as potable water and a waste pipe are accessible. You can mount it on a wall; you can let it stand on legs or a pedestal; or you can insert it into a countertop. Lavatories also come as part of a countertop; that is, the lavatory and the countertop are formed as a one-piece unit.

Sinks and lavatories are made from a variety of materials, including enameled cast iron and steel, vitreous china, stainless steel, cultured marble, and plastic. The only requirement is that the surface be smooth and non-absorbent and meet standards established by the American Society of Mechanical Engineers. The surface may stain or chip. You can often repair minor imperfections. (See page 28.) You cannot, however, fix a sink that is cracked and leaks. It has to be replaced.

Sink Styles

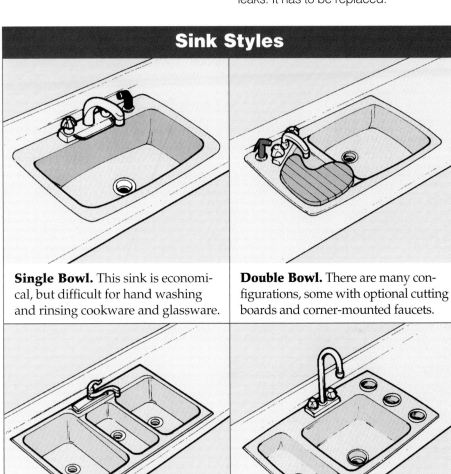

Single Bowl. This sink is economical, but difficult for hand washing and rinsing cookware and glassware.

Double Bowl. There are many configurations, some with optional cutting boards and corner-mounted faucets.

Triple Bowl. This unit needs about 12 in. more counter space than a double-bowl unit.

Bar Sink. A tall faucet is standard; an ice basin and garnish cups are optional.

Repairing Faucets:

Washer-Style Two-Handle

If you are not sure whether your two-handle faucet is equipped with washers or plastic cartridges, you will find out when you disassemble the unit.

Disassembly

Remove the screw holding the handle to the stem, and take off the handle. If the handle is outfitted with a cap, slip a utility knife under the cap and pry it off (Figure 1) to get at the screw holding the handle. A handle that is stubborn can often be loosened by tapping it from beneath with the handle of your screwdriver or a plastic-headed hammer. Easy does it. You do not want to crack the cap.

If you still can't free the handle, wrap electrical tape around the tip of a screwdriver; slide the tip under the handle; and pry using moderate pressure. Move the position of the screwdriver and again apply pressure. Keep repeating the procedure, moving the screwdriver around the entire circumference, until the handle loosens. This method also should be used if a handle is stuck in place because of corrosion.

If a handle is stubborn, you may have to use a handle puller (Figure 2).

When the handle is off, place an adjustable wrench on the stem retaining nut, and turn the wrench counterclockwise to loosen the nut (Figure 3). You can use adjustable pliers, but protect the nut by wrapping electrical tape around the jaws of the pliers. Turn the stem out of the faucet by hand. If the stem is tight, reattach the handle and use that for leverage.

Note: If the base of the stem does not have a washer, the faucet is the plastic cartridge design. (See pages 19 and 20.)

Leak from Spout

Remove the brass screw holding the washer to the stem (Figure 4). Take the total stem assembly with you when shopping for replacements to ensure the same sizes (Figure 5).

Attach the new washer to the stem with the new brass screw, tightening just enough to hold the washer securely.

If you have been experiencing frequent washer failure, the seat in the faucet against which the washer sits is probably damaged. You may

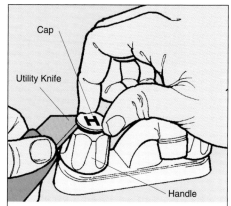

1 The handle screws in washer-style faucets are often hidden under caps. They can be removed by placing the tip of a utility knife under the cap and prying up.

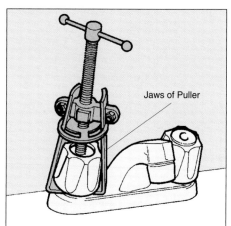

2 If using excessive force would cause damage to a handle that is frozen tightly to a stem, then a special puller will be needed.

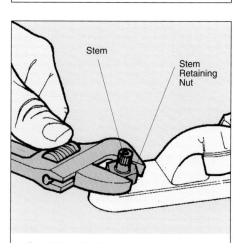

3 With the handle removed, use a wrench or adjustable pliers to loosen the stem retaining nut. Remove the part by hand.

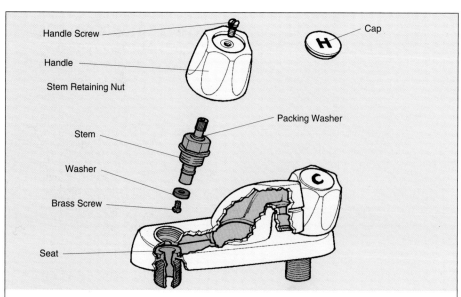

Washer-Style Two-Handle Faucet. Although styles have changed over the years, the internal parts of the compression or washer-style faucet have remained relatively the same.

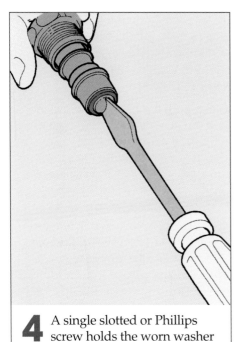

4 A single slotted or Phillips screw holds the worn washer to the stem. Use a conventional or Phillips screwdriver, respectively, to undo the screw.

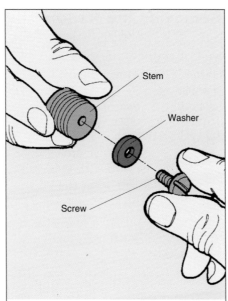

5 Replace each washer with one that fits the stem and the brass screw that holds the washer to the stem.

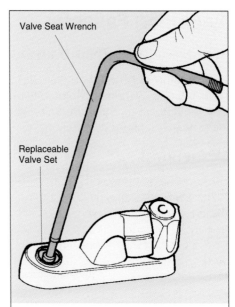

6 Seat damage occurs primarily from poor water quality. If this is causing washers to fail often, replace the seat (if possible).

be able to feel roughness by inserting your finger into the hole and moving it against the seat. Roughness often can be eliminated by rotating a valve-seat reamer against the seat a few revolutions. If this does not help, use a valve-seat wrench to replace a replaceable seat (Figure 6). A faucet that does not have replaceable seats will probably have to be replaced.

If stems are equipped with neoprene caps instead of washers, you may not be able to find replacements. The design was not popular. Take the stem with you to see if you can find new stems of the same configuration that use washers. If this fails, replace the faucet.

Leak from Around Handle

If tightening the stem retaining nut does not stop a leak (see Reassembly, below), the seal around the stem needs to be replaced. Depending upon the age of your faucet, the seal is either a graphite-impregnated, rope-like material called packing (Figure 7) that is wrapped around the

top of the stem, a packing washer that fits inside the stem retaining nut, or one or more small O-rings that fit into grooves in the stem (Figure 8). When purchasing replacements, take the stem with you to be certain you get what you need. If your stem uses O-rings, spread a thin coating of heat-proof grease or liquid dish soap on them before putting them on the stem.

Reassembly

Remove any precipitated minerals or calcification deposits from the metal or plastic part of the stem. If necessary, rub them off gently with fine (No. 000) steel wool. Place the stem back into the faucet, turning it clockwise by hand until it is tight.

Attach the handle, and turn on the water. If there is a chatter, the washer is loose. Remove the stem to tighten the washer a bit more. If water seeps out from around the handle, the stem retaining nut may not be tight enough. Remove the handle, and tighten until snug.

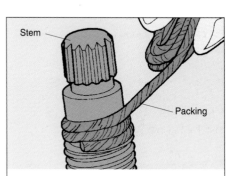

7 If the faucet is an old unit, it probably will require a winding of rope-type packing on the stem to prevent a leak.

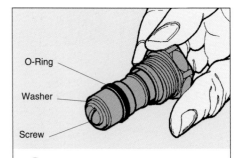

8 Modern faucets use O-rings to prevent leaks around handles If there is a leak, lift off the O-ring using the tip of an awl and replace with one of the same size.

Repairing Faucets:

Ceramic-Disc One-Handle

A ceramic-disc one-handle faucet consists of a cylinder in which there is a movable disc that rotates against a stationary disc to control the temperature of the water mixture.

If you do not know whether you have a ceramic-disc or ball-style one-handle faucet, you will find out as soon as you remove the handle.

Removing the Handle

Remove the handle by undoing the setscrew holding the handle (Figure 1) and then the cap, if there is one (Figure 2). The screw may be concealed under a cover or button.

Disassembly

If the problem is a leak around the handle, tightening the screws holding the ceramic-disc assembly should stop it.

To fix a leak from the spout, unscrew and remove the ceramic-disc assembly (Figure 3). Turn the cylinder upside down to remove the seals (Figure 4).

Clean both the base of the cylinder and the seats in which the seals sit (Figure 5). Flush with water to remove deposits that might be the reason for the leak.

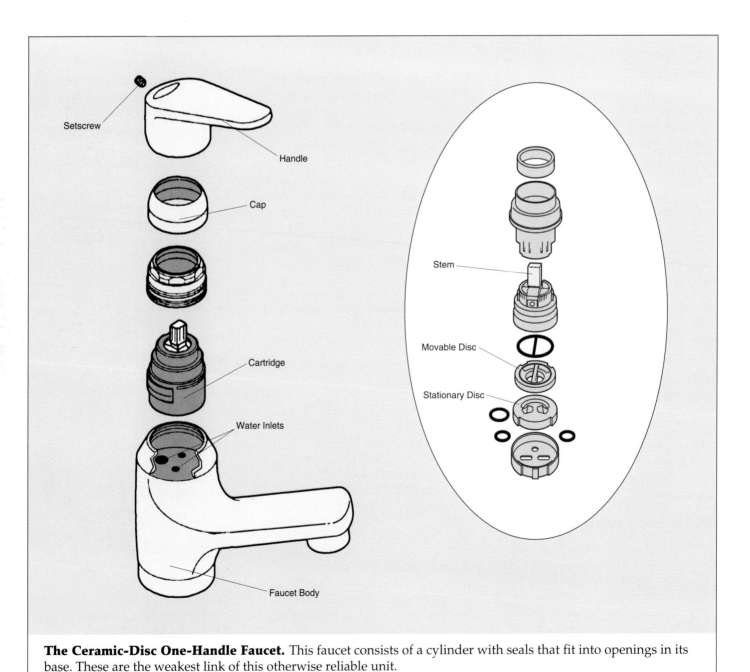

Setscrew

Handle

Cap

Cartridge

Water Inlets

Faucet Body

Stem

Movable Disc

Stationary Disc

The Ceramic-Disc One-Handle Faucet. This faucet consists of a cylinder with seals that fit into openings in its base. These are the weakest link of this otherwise reliable unit.

Reassembly

Reinsert and secure the ceramic-disc assembly. Avoid overtightening screws. Turn on the water to see if the leak has been fixed. If not, disassemble the faucet again, and replace the seals (Figure 6).

To ensure proper fit, make sure you buy seals that fit your particular make of faucet.

If seals do not resolve the problem, replace the ceramic-disc assembly. When replacing the handle, place it in a partially open position and slowly turn on the water shutoff valves. Restore the water slowly to prevent the cartridge from shattering. When water flows smoothly, turn off the faucet.

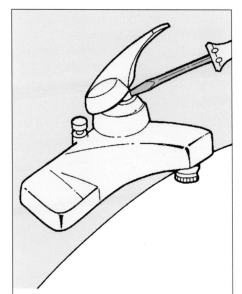

1 Begin repair by removing the setscrew, which may be a conventional straight-slot type, a Phillips-head screw, or an Allen screw.

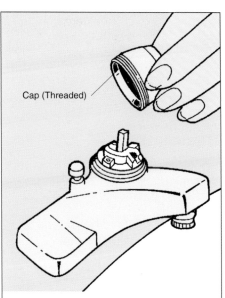

Cap (Threaded)

2 Remove the faucet-handle cap, which may or may not be threaded to the main faucet body.

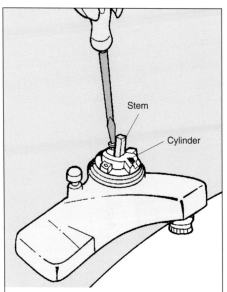

Stem

Cylinder

3 Undo the screws holding the cylinder, and remove it. If the cylinder sticks, grab the stem with pliers and pull.

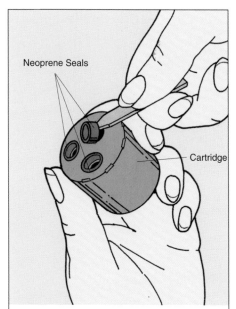

Neoprene Seals

Cartridge

4 Turn the cylinder upside down and carefully remove the neoprene seals using the point of a knife or scratch awl.

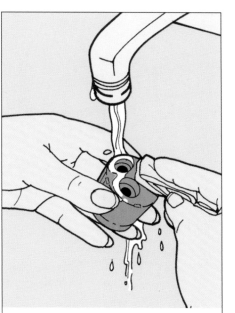

5 Clean the base of the cylinder and the seats in which seals sit. Be sure to flush the cylinder with water to get rid of deposits.

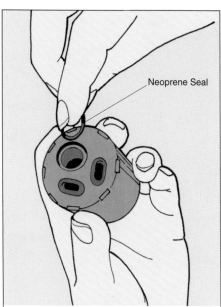

Neoprene Seal

6 Install new seals that fit your particular make of faucet. Reinsert the cylinder; tighten screws; and reassemble the other parts.

Repairing Faucets:

Ball-Type One-Handle

Of all faucets, this one is the most temperamental when it comes to repairs. The leak may seem to be fixed, only to reappear a few days later. You may have to exercise patience until the problem is finally resolved. Repair kits for this faucet are available containing individual parts or all parts, including the tension-ring spanner wrench.

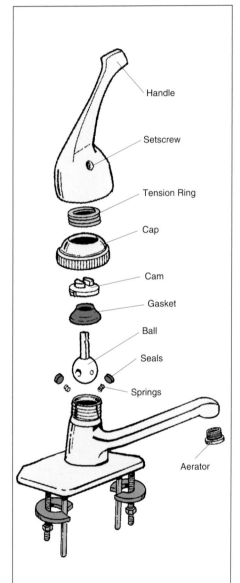

Ball-Type One-Handle Faucet.
A common variation of this faucet has a tension ring which, if loose, will allow water to drip from the spout.

Disassembly

Remove the handle, using a screwdriver or hex key (Figure 1). You will spot the tension ring, which is a threaded part with notches. Many times a leak is caused by a loose tension ring. Fit a tension-ring spanner wrench into the notches of the ring and tighten it (Figure 2). Reinstall parts and turn on the water to see if the leak has been fixed. If not, turn off the water and proceed to remove the handle, cover or cap, tension ring, cam, gasket, ball, seals, and springs (Figures 3–7).

Reassembly

Since it is usually not possible to determine which part is causing a leak, you can save yourself considerable time and effort by installing all new parts. Notice that seals and springs fit into water inlet ports with springs facing down into the part.

If the ball you take out of the faucet is plastic and your water tends to scale, replace it with another plastic ball.

Obviously, new parts of the unit are installed in the reverse order that you removed old parts out of the faucet. But there is one thing to watch out for. The cam will probably have a tiny key on it (Figure 8). The key should fit securely into the keyway in the faucet housing.

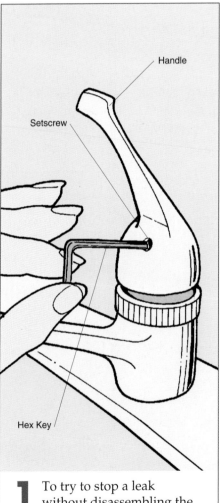

1 To try to stop a leak without disassembling the faucet, first loosen the handle setscrew and remove the handle.

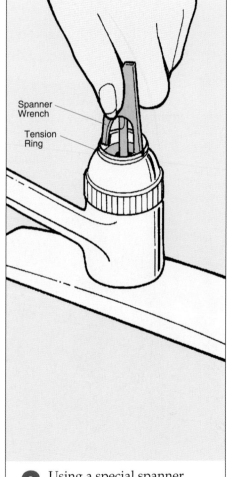

2 Using a special spanner wrench, tighten the adjustable tension ring. Be sure to use a spanner wrench for your make of faucet.

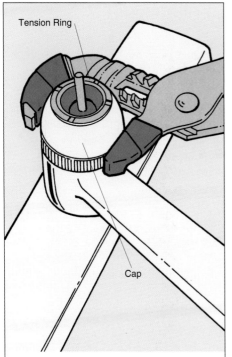

Tension Ring

Cap

3 If tightening the tension ring does not get results, rebuild the faucet. After removing the handle, loosen and remove the cap and tension ring.

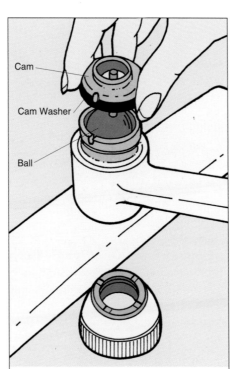

Cam

Cam Washer

Ball

4 Place a rag around the base of the spout to absorb water that may splash, and lift off the cam and washer. Then lift the spout off the faucet body.

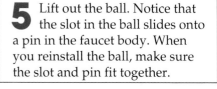

Slot

Pin

5 Lift out the ball. Notice that the slot in the ball slides onto a pin in the faucet body. When you reinstall the ball, make sure the slot and pin fit together.

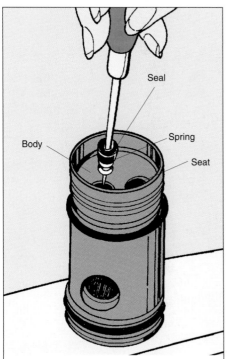

Seal

Body

Spring

Seat

6 Remove the seals and springs in the faucet body, and replace them with new parts contained in a repair kit for your make of faucet.

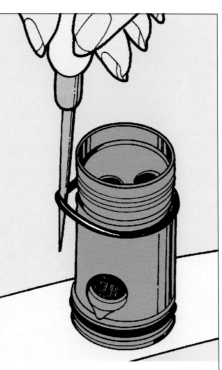

7 If water has been leaking from around the base of the spout of a swivel faucet, also install new O-rings. Lubricate the rings with heat-proof grease.

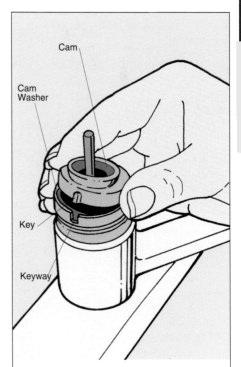

Cam

Cam Washer

Key

Keyway

8 In reassembling the faucet, make sure that the lug of the cam fits securely into the notch of the faucet body.

Repairing Faucets:

Tipping-Valve One-Handle

Occasionally, a particle in the water will be deposited on one of the seats and prevent a tipping valve from closing all the way. Before you disassemble the faucet, you may be able to flush the particle away by opening and closing the faucet quickly a few times.

Disassembly

Unscrew and remove the spout (Figure 1). If the spout nut is stuck, use adjustable pliers to loosen it, but wrap electrical tape around plier jaws so you do not scar the spout.

Lift off the cover (Figure 2), and use a screwdriver to remove slotted nuts over tipping valves. Remove the tipping valves (Figure 3).

Making the Repair

In all likelihood, the leak is caused by a damaged valve seat. Tipping valves seldom go bad.

Using a valve-seat wrench, remove valve seats.

Get matching replacements from your local hardware, home-center, or plumbing-supply store, and install the new seats.

Reinstall the tipping valves so the valve stems are facing down into the faucet.

Put the cover and spout back on, and turn on the water.

If the leak persists, one or both tipping valves are faulty. Disassemble the unit again, but this time replace the tipping valves.

If there is a leak from around the base of the spout, replace the O-ring before screwing the spout back onto the faucet (Figure 4). Lubricate the O-ring with heat-proof grease.

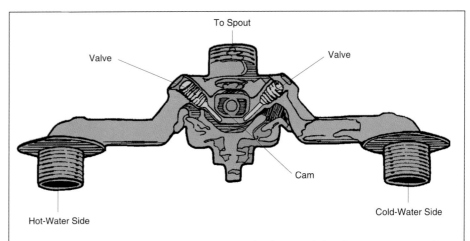

Tipping-Valve One-Handle Faucet. The heart of this faucet is a cam that rotates when you turn the handle. In this position, the cam is not engaging the tipping valve, therefore, the faucet is turned off.

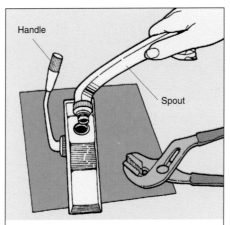

1 To begin repair, unscrew and remove the spout. Notice the unique position of the handle.

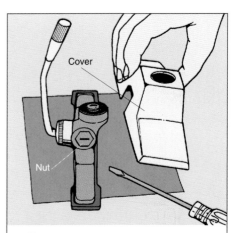

2 When the spout is off, the cover can be removed to reveal a slotted nut on each side of the faucet body.

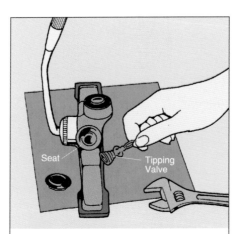

3 Remove the nut, which allows you to remove the tipping valve. You can now replace the seat and/or the tipping valve.

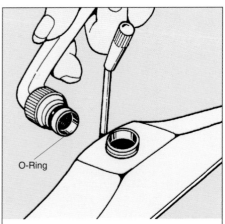

4 If there is a leak from around the base of the spout, replace the O-ring before screwing the spout back onto the faucet.

Repairing Faucets: Two-Handle Compression and Nylon Cartridge Style

The earliest faucets were made with compression mechanisms, consisting mainly of a threaded brass stem, a stem carriage with packing seal, a renewable seat washer, and a brass seat. The stem compresses the washer against its seat and stops the flow. Two-handle faucets are really mixing valves, allowing you to blend hot and cold water in any combination.

Some seats are replaceable—they thread out with a special wrench—while others are not. If you look into the faucet body and see a square or hex-shaped wrenching surface in the center of the seat, it's replaceable. If not, and the seat has voids in the sealing surface, all you can do is grind the seat down with a seat-dressing tool.

The cartridge faucet's advantage is that it takes the user's bad habits out of the picture. You can't over-tighten a cartridge handle, while compression faucets are tightened differently by each user. Overtightening ruins the washer, and if not soon replaced, water seeping past it will cut a channel in the seat surface.

The key to a good compression faucet repair is a smooth seat and heat-proof grease. Grease preserves the washer and the seat, and doesn't dissolve. When the repair is made, remind everyone that a repaired faucet doesn't need as heavy a hand as a leaky one.

Repairing Nylon-Cartridge Faucets

Nylon cartridges are used on a lot of entry-level two-handle faucets. They're easy and economical to service. Just turn off the water; remove the faucet handle and cartridge nut; then lift the cartridge from the faucet body. You should see a spring-loaded, cup-shaped rubber seal in the base of the faucet port. Buy a replacement and reinstall the cartridge. If the leak persists, replace the entire cartridge. You'll need to find an exact replacement.

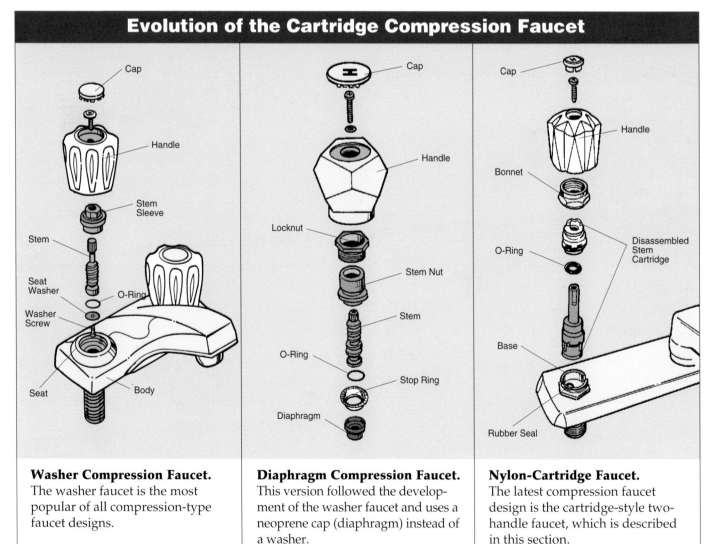

Evolution of the Cartridge Compression Faucet

Washer Compression Faucet. The washer faucet is the most popular of all compression-type faucet designs.

Diaphragm Compression Faucet. This version followed the development of the washer faucet and uses a neoprene cap (diaphragm) instead of a washer.

Nylon-Cartridge Faucet. The latest compression faucet design is the cartridge-style two-handle faucet, which is described in this section.

Repairing Faucets:

Cartridge-Style One-Handle

Disassembly

This type of one-handle faucet is a more difficult project due to the fact that the fastener holding the cartridge in the faucet may be difficult to spot and, therefore, to remove.

The problem involves a cartridge retaining clip, which is either on the inside under the handle or on the outside of the faucet.

Closely examine the outside of the faucet body below the handle for a ridge projecting out of the body. If you spot one, it is probably the retaining clip (Figure 1). Using pliers, grip the stem and pry or pull out the clip (Figure 2). When this has been done, twist or lift the handle and cartridge out

of the faucet (Figure 3). Separate the handle and cartridge.

If there is no opening in the faucet body, find the screw holding the handle (Figure 4). It might be under a cap that you have to pry off (Figure 5). Then again, it might be at the base of the handle, so you will have to lift the handle to get at the screw (Figure 6).

Once the handle is off, you will see the cartridge. At the top of the cartridge, there might be a decorative retainer sleeve (Figure 7). Remove that to get at the cartridge retaining clip. Pry or pull the clip out, and then remove the cartridge (Figure 8).

Repair

The repair is made by replacing the cartridge. A hardware, home-center, or plumbing-supply store that sells your particular brand of faucet will be able to supply you with the new part.

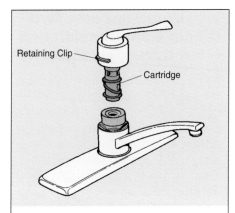

1 You may find an external retaining clip that has to be removed in order to free a cartridge. The handle is held to the cartridge by a screw, probably an Allen screw.

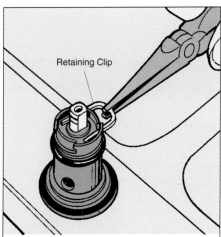

2 The retaining clip can be easily removed with needle-nose pliers.

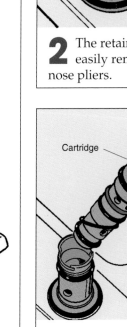

3 Grasp the cartridge stem with pliers, and pull the part from the faucet body. Replace the cartridge.

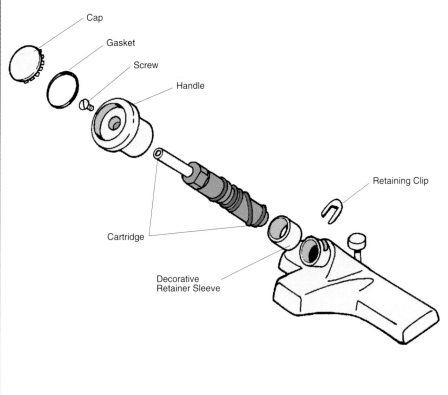

Cartridge-Style One-Handle Faucet. Here are the parts that have to be removed to replace the cartridge. In order, they are a cap, gasket, screw, handle, decorative retainer sleeve, retaining clip, and cartridge.

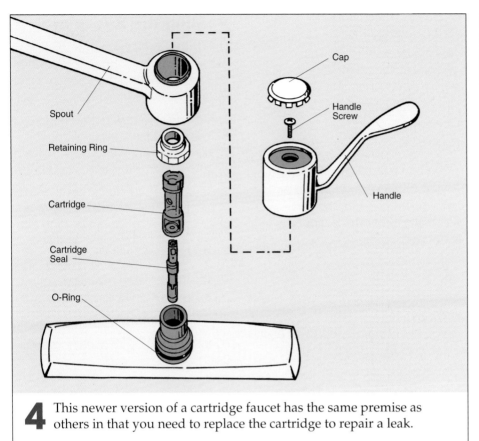

Spout

Retaining Ring

Cartridge

Cartridge Seal

O-Ring

Cap

Handle Screw

Handle

4 This newer version of a cartridge faucet has the same premise as others in that you need to replace the cartridge to repair a leak.

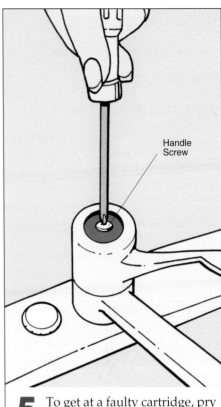

Handle Screw

5 To get at a faulty cartridge, pry off the cap over the handle screw, and remove the screw.

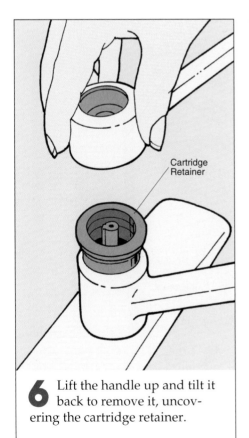

Cartridge Retainer

6 Lift the handle up and tilt it back to remove it, uncovering the cartridge retainer.

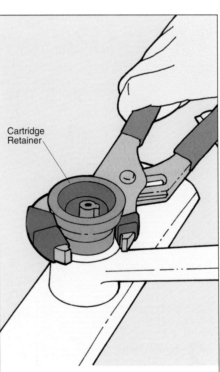

Cartridge Retainer

7 To remove the retainer, grab it with adjustable pliers and turn counterclockwise. You may also find a retaining clip.

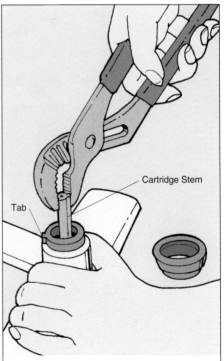

Cartridge Stem

Tab

8 Grasp the cartridge stem and pull it from the faucet body. The tab on the cartridge faces toward the front of the faucet.

Repairing Faucets:

From the Baseplate

When water seeps out from around the baseplate of a faucet, the gasket or plumber's putty that was installed under the baseplate has probably deteriorated. Here's how to remove the faucet and restore the seal.

Removing the Faucet

Examine the water lines leading to the faucet to find fittings that connect the lines to the faucet. Using an adjustable or basin wrench, loosen these fittings and disconnect the lines from the faucet (Figures 1 and 2).

Slip the wrench onto one of the faucet mounting nuts holding the faucet to the sink. Turn the wrench counterclockwise to remove the nut.

Then, remove the faucet mounting nut on the other side. Use a lubricant if the mounting nuts are stuck because of corrosion. Wipe away any excess (Figure 3).

If working on a lavatory, disconnect the pop-up stopper (Figure 4). Release the lift rod holding the lever by unscrewing the clevis screw and disconnect the spring clip. Then unscrew the retaining nut and turn the pivot rod, if necessary, and detach the rod from the stopper.

If working on a kitchen sink, you may have to release the hose feeding water to the spray unit (Figure 5).

With parts that have been attached to the faucet now released, lift the faucet and gasket (if there is a gasket) off the sink (Figure 6). Discard the gasket.

Sealing the Baseplate

Use a putty knife to clean off particles of the old gasket or putty from the sink and the faucet baseplate (Figure 7). Both areas have to be clean.

Then install the new gasket (Figure 8), or spread latex caulk or silicone sealant around the entire baseplate (Figure 9).

Reseat the faucet and press it down against the sink. A line of putty or silicone should ooze out beyond the baseplate (if you are using putty or silicone).

Reattach the faucet mounting nuts. Reattach lines and lavatory pop-up stopper or sink spray unit hose. Then, use a utility knife to trim off excess putty or silicone (if you are using putty or silicone).

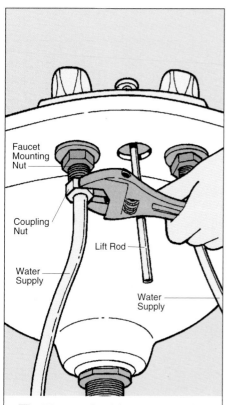

1 Hot- and cold-water supply lines, which are connected with compression fittings, can be disconnected from the faucet using an adjustable wrench.

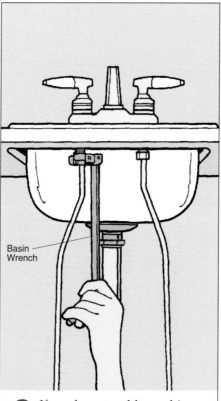

2 If you have trouble reaching fasteners, use a basin wrench. It allows you to loosen and tighten inaccessible fittings with an adjustable wrench.

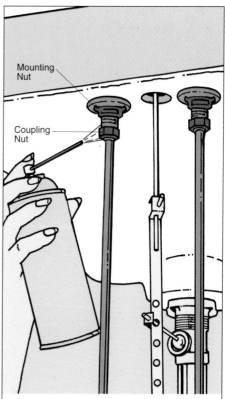

3 If faucet mounting nuts are stuck because of corrosion, spray them with a penetrating lubricant. Let the lubricant seep in for several minutes before attempting to free nuts.

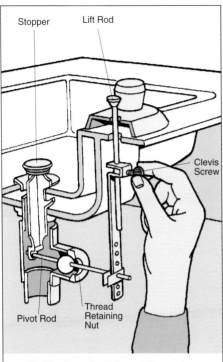

4 To free the lift rod from the faucet of a lavatory, simply unscrew the clevis screw and pull out the lift rod.

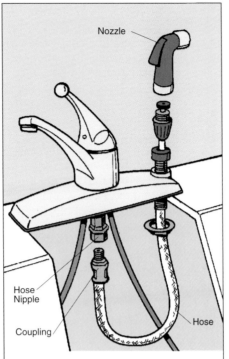

5 With many sinks, you must free the spray hose at the faucet. This is done by unscrewing the coupling nut from the spray outlet shank of the faucet.

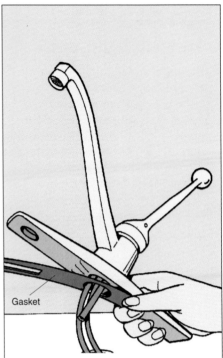

6 Remove the faucet and gasket, if there is a gasket. Discard the gasket, especially if it is damaged.

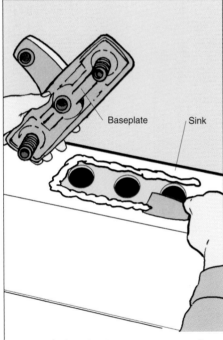

7 If plumber's putty was used instead of a gasket to seal the baseplate of the faucet, scrape the old putty off the mounting surface of the sink and off the faucet. Both surfaces must be clean.

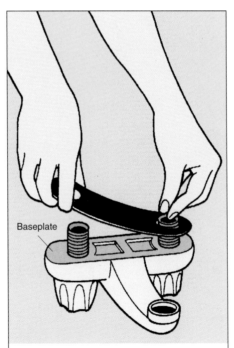

8 Whether you use a gasket (shown), latex caulk, or silicone sealant (Step 9) is up to you. Some plumbers contend that gaskets tend to dry out and fail quicker than putty.

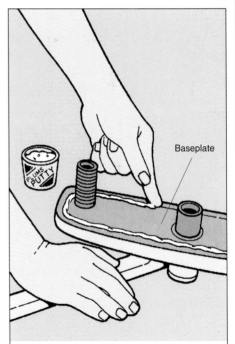

9 If you do not use the gasket, apply a ⅛-in. bead of latex or silicone caulk around the perimeter of the baseplate. Reinstall the faucet, and wipe away any excess sealant.

Repairing Spray Attachments

If little or no water comes out of the spray head of a sink's spray attachment, look under the sink to see that the hose that extends from the faucet to the spray unit is straight (Figure 1). If it is kinked, water cannot get through to the spray head. You may have to disconnect the hose to straighten it (Figure 2). If the hose is straight, the reason for a restricted spray could be a dirty spray head nozzle (Figure 3).

Unscrew the nozzle from the head; wash it out; soak it in vinegar; or use a thin piece of wire to remove mineral deposits (Figure 4). If it does not come clean, you can buy a replacement. To clean the other parts of the spray attachment, turn on the water and press the spray head handle before screwing the nozzle back into the spray head.

If none of these procedures are effective in restoring the spray, unscrew the faucet-spout nut. The deck fitting has a threaded plastic shank with a jamb nut. It is accessed from below. Remove the spout, and lift or screw the diverter valve from the faucet (Figures 5 and 6).

Open the cold- or hot-water faucet slowly so water gushes from the vacated hole where the diverter valve sits. This will flush out residue that may be impeding the diverter valve.

Wash the diverter valve with a brush saturated with vinegar (Figure 7); then reinstall it and the faucet spout. Try the spray. If the restriction persists, replace the diverter valve.

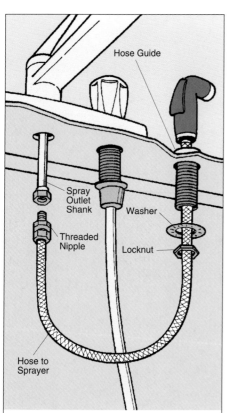

1 If the spray attachment malfunctions, check that the hose is straight. You may have to disconnect it from the spray outlet shank in order to straighten it.

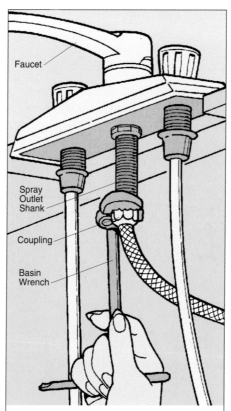

2 If you can't get at the coupling of a spray hose, use a basin wrench. It gives you more flexibility than an adjustable or open-end wrench.

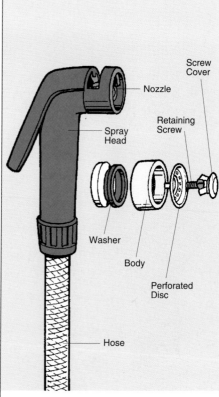

3 Usually you can flush deposits from the spray-head assembly, but you may have to disassemble it entirely for cleaning.

Spray Disc

4 Soak the pieces in vinegar for a few hours, or use a thin piece of wire to remove any mineral deposits that may be clogging the spray disc.

Spout Nut
O-Ring
Diverter Valve
Nozzle
Spray Head
Hose Nut
Washer
Hose
Snap Ring
Coupling
Groove for Snap Ring

5 The diverter valve of a spray attachment for a two-handle faucet lies beneath the spout. Remove the spout to service, or replace the diverter valve.

Diverter Valve

6 Diverter valves for spray attachments coupled to one-handle faucets are usually positioned in the front or back of the faucet body. You will probably have to disassemble the faucet to reach it.

Diverter Valve

7 After pulling the diverter valve out of the faucet body, clean it with a brush saturated with vinegar. If this fails to work, replace the diverter.

Cleaning an Aerator

An aerator is screwed into the nozzle of every sink and lavatory spout to lessen the force of the flow of water from the nozzle (top). If the flow ever seems sluggish, the aerator may be clogged.

Removing an aerator from a nozzle is not a difficult task, but do it carefully to keep from damaging the part. If the aerator cannot be unscrewed by hand, wrap electrical tape around the jaws of pliers, engage the aerator with the pliers, and turn counter-clockwise to loosen the aerator. Then, unscrew it by hand.

Flush deposits from the aerator screen. Use an old toothbrush to loosen stubborn residue (bottom). If cleaning does not improve the flow of water, replace the aerator. Screw it on hand-tight.

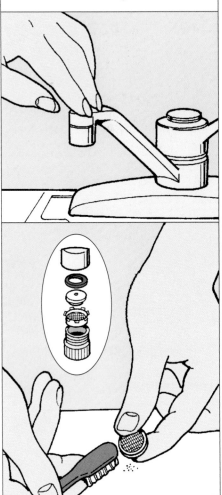

Repairing Faucets:

Leak From Base of Spout

Disassembly

If water leaks from around the base of a swivel spout of the type used in kitchen and utility-room sinks, loosen the swivel nut holding the spout to the faucet (Figure 1). Use adjustable pliers, but wrap electrical tape around the jaws to keep from putting scars into the nut. Loosen the nut all the way and pull the spout free.

Making the Repair

You should find an O-ring around the threaded portion of the spout. Use the point of a knife or scratch awl to remove the O-ring from its place (Figure 2). Get a replacement of the same size. Spread a thin coat of heat-proof grease or liquid dish soap over it, and put it into position on the spout. A different style is illustrated in Figures 3, 4, and 5.

Reassembly

Screw the spout back onto the faucet by hand until you cannot turn the swivel nut. Be careful that you do not cross-thread the nut and its seat in the faucet. Using adjustable pliers, turn the swivel nut ⅛ turn more (Figure 6). Open the faucet. If there is a leak around the spout, tighten the swivel nut ⅛ turn at a time until it stops.

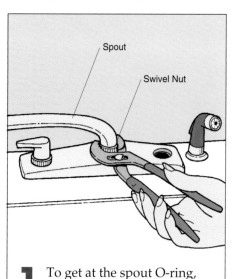

1 To get at the spout O-ring, loosen the swivel nut that holds the spout to the faucet. Tape the jaws of the pliers.

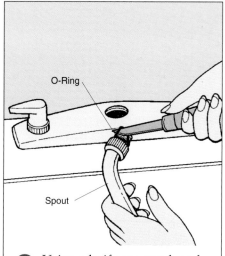

2 Using a knife or scratch awl, remove and discard the damaged O-ring, replacing it with one of the same size.

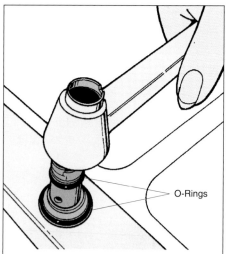

3 Newer swivel spouts (shown here and in subsequent figures) still requires replacement of O-rings when water leaks.

4 You can cut off the worn O-rings sealing a swivel faucet with a sharp knife. Before installing new O-rings, coat them with a heat-resistant lubricant.

5 Clean deposits from inside the spout cover with fine steel wool, sand cloth, or by soaking the spout in vinegar. Seat the spout securely on the faucet body.

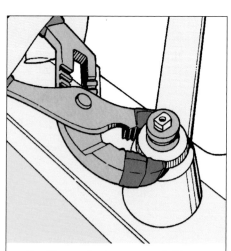

6 The swivel spouts of all faucets are held to the assembly in some way. Here, with this cartridge faucet, it's by means of a retaining nut.

Repairing Leaky Supply Risers

Hot- and cold-water supply risers (supply lines), extending to a faucet from the water pipes may in time begin to leak. If water shutoff valves exist, the repair is simple to make.

If the leak is from the nut connecting the supply line to the valve port of the shutoff valve on the water pipe, close the shutoff valve.

Using an adjustable wrench, undo the nut that attaches the line to the port. Slide the nut up onto the line and carefully pull the line out of its seat in the valve port until the ferrule (usually brass) on the line is completely exposed.

The ferrule provides a seal between the shutoff valve and the supply riser. If the ferrule is damaged, the seal will be broken.

Wrap a layer of Teflon tape around the ferrule. Reinsert the end of the

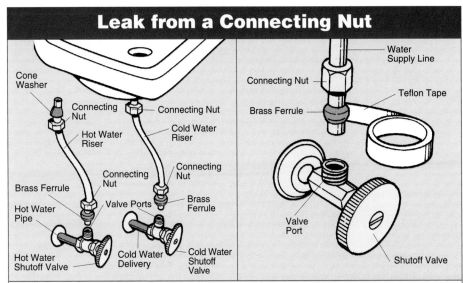

Leak from a Connecting Nut

Shown are the particular parts you have to deal with when repairing a leaking hot- or cold-water riser (left). A leak from around the nut that connects a metal supply line to the valve ports (right) can often be sealed using Teflon tape.

line into the valve port so that the ferrule is secure. Slide the nut down and turn it by hand until it is tight. Then, using the adjustable wrench, turn the nut one full turn.

Open the shutoff valve; turn on the water; and check to see if the leak has stopped. If not, turn the nut a little at a time with the wrench until the leak has ceased.

Replacing a Water Supply Riser

When a fixture supply riser begins to leak, it's often best to replace it with a braided stainless-steel riser.

Shut off the water under the fixture; use a small adjustable wrench to loosen the compression nut on the valve or adapter. Follow by threading the coupling nut from the faucet shank. If the coupling nut is

easy to reach, use an adjustable wrench.

Apply just a touch of pipe joint compound or liquid soap to the ground joint surfaces inside the riser's fittings; then thread the larger fitting onto the faucet shank. Tighten until it feels snug. If your faucet has a threaded brass fitting soldered to a soft copper tube, you'll need to backhold the faucet

fitting as you tighten the riser fitting.

Finally, thread the compression fitting onto the shutoff valve's port, and tighten until it feels snug. Don't let the tube turn as you tighten the nut. Turn the water on and test your work. If you see a leak, tighten the fitting just a little more.

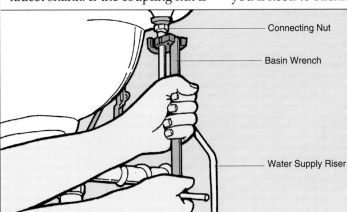

When there isn't enough clearance to get at upper connecting nuts, use a basin wrench.

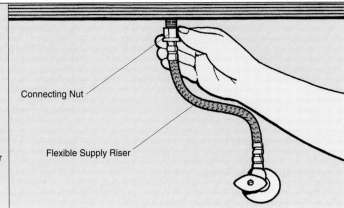

Insert the ends of the braided supply line into their respective seats and tighten the compression nuts.

Repairing a Porcelain Enamel Sink

To repair a chip in a porcelain enamel sink, buy a color-matched porcelain repair kit. If you can't find a match, mix the repair compound with alkyd-based paint that matches the sink color. Test on an inconspicuous area first.

1. Using a piece of medium-grit emery cloth, sand the chipped area. Remove all soap scum and rust, but avoid sanding beyond the damaged spot. Clean the spot using a cloth dampened with rubbing alcohol. Wait for the alcohol to dry.

2. Mix the repair compound as per package directions.

3. Scoop a little of the compound onto a single-edged razor blade and apply it to the damaged area. Scrape off excess until the compound lies flush with the surrounding surface.

4. After the patch dries, dip a cotton swab in fingernail polish remover, and remove excess repair compound to blend the edges into the porcelain.

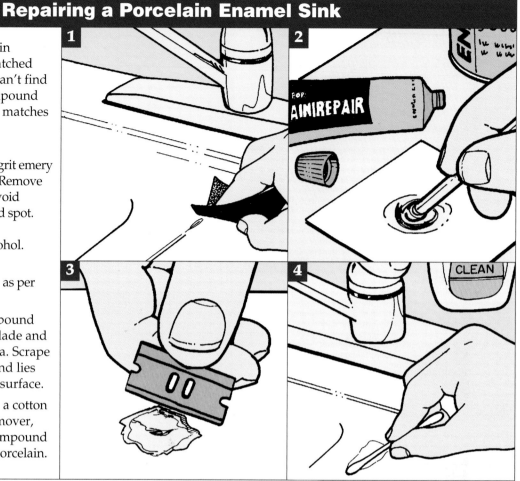

Sealing the Joint Between Sink & Cabinet

Brush out crumbled pieces of old caulking and clean with an alcohol-dampened cloth. Allow it to dry.

1. Apply a strip of ½-inch-wide masking tape on and around the sink to protect it. The edge of the tape should lie just above the joint formed by the sink rim and cabinet.

2. Snip off the end of a tube of caulk to provide the narrowest bead of caulk possible. Slowly move around the rim, filling the joint with caulk. Next, dip your finger into water and run it around the caulking to smooth the bead.

3. Allow caulking to cure for several hours. Then, carefully pull off the masking tape, and use a single-edged razor blade to remove caulking that has gotten on the sink.

4. Use a putty knife to remove any excess on the countertop.

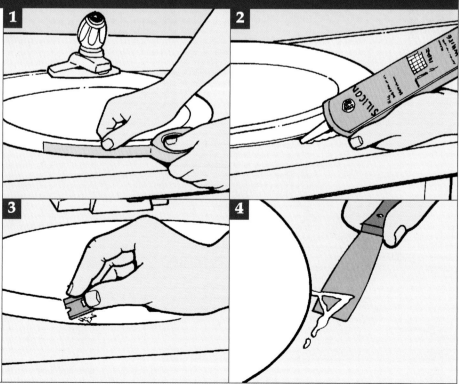

toilets

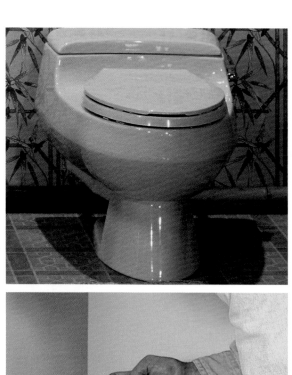

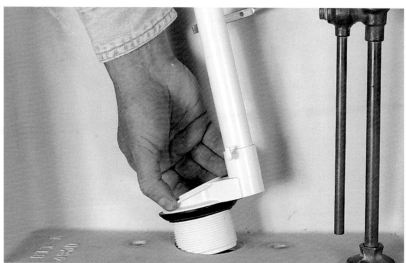

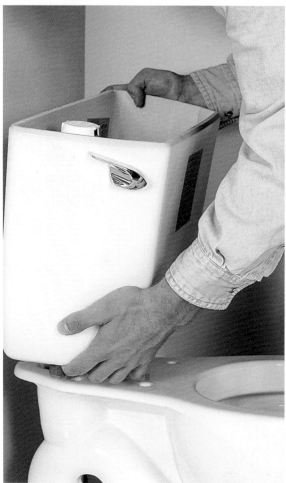

Anatomy of a Toilet

Most residential toilets consist of a tank and a bowl with an integral base attached to the floor. Others are mounted on the wall so the bowl is off the floor and the tank sits on top of the bowl. A toilet can have a separate tank and bowl, or they can be manufactured as one piece.

When you flush a gravity-operated toilet, gravity forces water to rush from the tank into the bowl. This surging water creates a siphon within the trap that pulls the contents out of the bowl into the drain.

The mechanisms inside the tank are involved either with the replenishment of water into the tank from the home's water supply system or the discharge of water from the tank into the bowl.

Water-Intake System

The water-intake system consists of a water-supply riser connected to a water-intake valve and a float. The water-supply riser is attached to a water-shutoff valve.

There are two types of water inlet: a traditional ballcock, which has a float ball; and intake valves that have other kinds of floats. These usually ride up and down on the central valve column. Some columns are adjustable to fit variously-sized tanks

A more recent design has the float as part of the ballcock. Another does away with the float altogether and incorporates a pressure-sensitive component that senses when the water level has dropped below the preset level.

There are only two things that can be done with this type of ballcock: you can lower or raise the water level in the tank by turning the adjustment screw counterclockwise or clockwise, respectively; and if the ballcock fails to control the intake of water as it should, you have to replace the entire assembly. Always install an antisiphon ballcock, which prevents tank water from entering the

potable water supply if a vacuum occurs on the line.

Water-Outlet System

The water-outlet system inside a toilet tank consists of a flush valve (rubber ball or flapper) that sits over a wide opening we call the flush-valve seat, and the overflow tube, which allows water to flow out of the tank into the bowl should the ballcock fail to shut.

The Bowl

As water flows out of the tank, it enters the bowl through several small holes around the rim of the bowl and through a larger opening called the siphon jet hole. The water's velocity pushes the bowl contents up through a discharge channel (or trap) into the drain. Water that sits in the bowl blocks sewer gases from entering the bathroom.

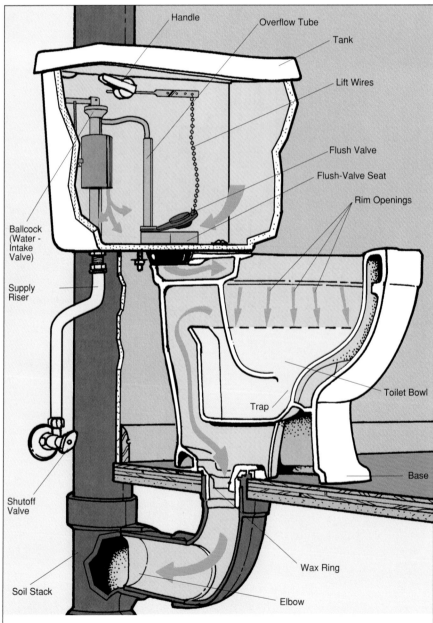

Gravity-Operated Flush Toilet. Flush toilets are basically the same from one unit to another although there are variations in the design of some components. One of the oldest ballcock designs is shown above.

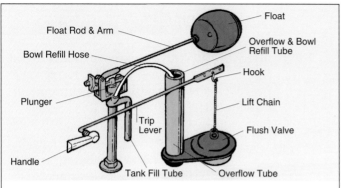

Ballcock Toilet. When the toilet is flushed the ball and float arm drop, opening the brass water-intake port.

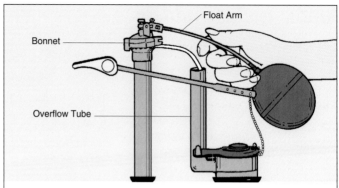

Anti-Siphon Ballcock Toilet. When the toilet is flushed the ball and float arm drop, opening the rubber diaphragm water-intake port in the plastic bonnet.

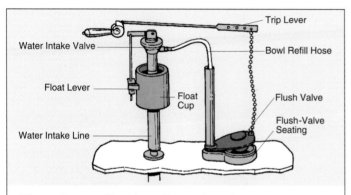

Float-Cup Ballcock Toilet. When the toilet is flushed, the float slides down the ballcock, drawing a diaphragm off the water-intake port.

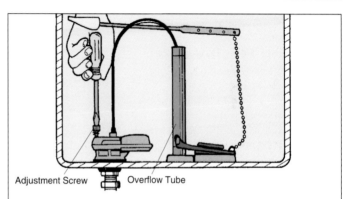

Pressure-Sensitive Intake Valve. When the toilet is flushed, the ballcock senses the water level has dropped below the preset level and opens the water-intake port.

Replacing a Toilet Seat

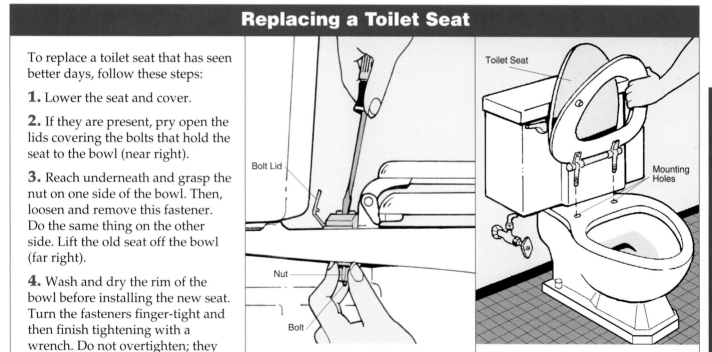

To replace a toilet seat that has seen better days, follow these steps:

1. Lower the seat and cover.

2. If they are present, pry open the lids covering the bolts that hold the seat to the bowl (near right).

3. Reach underneath and grasp the nut on one side of the bowl. Then, loosen and remove this fastener. Do the same thing on the other side. Lift the old seat off the bowl (far right).

4. Wash and dry the rim of the bowl before installing the new seat. Turn the fasteners finger-tight and then finish tightening with a wrench. Do not overtighten; they could crack.

Lift the bolt lid, hold the bolt with a screwdriver, and unscrew the nut.

Remove the old seat, and install the new one.

3 Toilets

Water Trickles into Bowl

or Phantom Flushes

Water trickling into the bowl most often is the result of a deteriorated flush valve (rubber ball or flapper). Sometimes, it is caused by a dirty flush-valve seat, which is preventing the ball or flapper from seating securely. The problem also could be caused by a defective ballcock or intake valve.

The toilet may seem to flush itself momentarily. This brief rush of water into the bowl, called a phantom flush, is caused by a faulty flush valve.

Servicing Flush-Valve Seat

With the water shutoff valve closed, flush the toilet. Use a large sponge to sop up remaining water. Wipe the flush valve seat with rags to clean off slime. For stubborn deposits, use fine steel wool if the rim is brass or a pad made for cleaning vinyl-coated cooking utensils if it is made of plastic.

Replacing Flapper Valve

If your toilet has a flapper valve, unhook its chain from the handle lever. Note in which hole in the lever the chain is hooked. If the flapper is attached to lugs on the side of the overflow tube, unhook it from those lugs. If it fits over the overflow tube instead, slide it off. Install the new flapper valve the same way.

Repositioning Rubber Ball

If the tank ball in your toilet is slimy and leaks, replace it. Holding the ball in one hand, lift the wire and back it from the ball threads; then install a new ball. Wipe the seat clean. If the threaded brass insert tears free of the ball, grip it with pliers and back the wire out.

If the new ball doesn't fall squarely on the valve seat, loosen the screw on the lift wire guide and move everything about $1/16$ inch. Test the ball through several flushes. If it still slips to one side, adjust it again. It often takes two or three small adjustments.

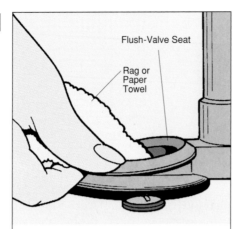

Servicing Flush-Valve Seat. The first step in stopping a trickle into the bowl from the tank is to clean the flush-valve seat.

Replacing Flapper Valve. Unhook the old flapper from the lugs on the overflow pipe (as illustrated) or slide it off the overflow pipe.

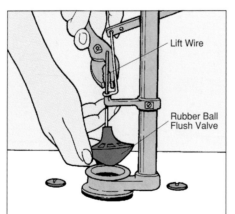

Repositioning Rubber Ball. Make sure the rubber ball falls squarely into the flush-valve seat. Replace a defective rubber ball by unscrewing it from the lift wire.

1. With the water shutoff valve closed, flush the toilet; sop up any water on the bottom of the tank; and disconnect the riser.

2. With a two-piece toilet, separate the tank from the bowl by undoing the tank bolts. These will be brass-on-brass. Use a large screwdriver in the tank.

3. Carefully lift the bowl from the tank and turn it upside down on the floor. Remove the soft rubber spud washer from the flush-valve threads, and lay the tank on its side. While holding the valve's overflow, loosen and remove the valve's spud nut.

4. Use a putty knife to clean any old pipe dope or plumber's putty from the area around the opening.

5. Slide the beveled washer onto the flush valve spud, and coat it with pipe joint compound. Feed the spud through the tank opening orienting the valve so the overflow backs up to the ballcock. Thread on the spud washer, and snug it down. Apply pipe dope to the tank bolt washers, and bolt the tank to the bowl. Expect the tank to feel wobbly until it's filled with water.

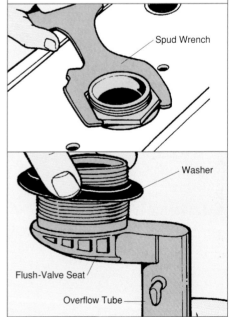

Water Flows Constantly into Bowl

When water will not stop running into the bowl, try jiggling the handle to dislodge the stuck flush-valve (rubber ball or flapper) handle assembly. If this does not work, the fault lies with a flapper chain or lift wire adjustment.

Repairing Handle Assembly

If jiggling the handle stops the flow of water, the handle assembly is probably sticking because of mineral deposits on the mechanism.

With the water shutoff valve closed, flush the toilet. Using an adjustable wrench, loosen the nut holding the handle to the inner wall of the tank. Clean lime deposits off the threads of the handle mechanism with a wire brush saturated with vinegar. Flush with water. Then, tighten the nut securely. If this does not work, the next step is to check on the lift wire or chain.

If the handle assembly lifts a tank ball, it has a lift wire. If the lower lift wire is bent, unscrew the rubber ball; slide the lower wire away from the upper wire to disconnect it; and straighten or replace the wire.

If the handle assembly uses a chain to draw a flapper flush valve off the flush-valve seat, the chain probably has too much slack. Unhook the chain from the hole in the handle lever and switch it to another hole to reduce the slack. There should be about ½ inch of slack to the chain. If the chain is too long, use needle-nose pliers to remove links, which will reduce the length.

Servicing the Float

If jiggling the handle does not stop the flow of water into the bowl, the float is lying too low in the water and is keeping the water-inlet valve from closing. The float is not adjusted properly or it is too heavy. A heavy float can result when the hollow float ball develops a hole that allows water to get inside it. In either case, the result can be a float that does not rise to a level that is sufficient to allow the water-inlet valve to close.

Water will rise above the top of the overflow tube and pour into the bowl through that tube. If you remove the tank lid, you will be able to see this. Do the following: turn the float onto the threaded float arm and flush the toilet. Does the water again rise over the top of the overflow and bowl-refill tube? If the answer is "yes," flush the toilet with the water shutoff valve closed. Unscrew the float and replace it with a new one.

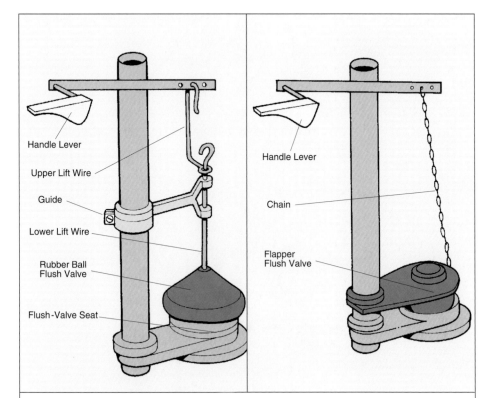

Handling Assembly Repairs. The lift wire must not be bent if a rubber ball flush valve (left) is to fall squarely into the flush-valve seat. Slack in the chain to a flapper flush valve (right) should be about ½ in. If greater, move the chain to another hole to reduce the slack.

Handle Lever
Upper Lift Wire
Guide
Lower Lift Wire
Rubber Ball Flush Valve
Flush-Valve Seat

Handle Lever
Chain
Flapper Flush Valve

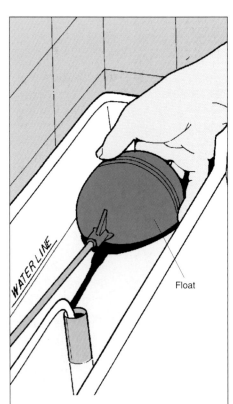

Servicing the Float. Lift the float. If the flow of water stops, tighten or replace the float.

WATER LINE
Float

3 Toilets

Water Trickles Constantly into Tank

Servicing the Float

For information on this procedure, see page 33.

Servicing the Ballcock

The method of repairing the ballcock depends upon its design style. In all cases, when you reassemble the ballcock, use a nylon pad to clean sediment from the water-intake port before installing the plunger.
To service the ballcock, first shut off water supply and flush the toilet.

1 **Traditional-Style Brass Ballcock.** Remove the wing nut or screw holding the float rod to the ballcock, and remove the float rod and float. Pry the plunger out of the ballcock.

Take the plunger to a plumbing-supply or home-center store to determine if replacement seals or a new plunger is available. If so, buy one or the other and reassemble the unit.

2 **Traditional-Style Plastic Ballcock.** Remove the screws holding the top of the ballcock and lift it off. If parts are corroded or cracked, replace the ballcock. If parts look okay, replace the seals on the plunger and the diaphragm if these parts are available.

3 **Plastic Float Ballcock.** With a ballcock that uses a round plastic float that encircles the ballcock, lift off the ballcock cap; press down on the plunger; and turn it to lift it off. If parts look sound, remove the seal from inside the plunger and replace it.

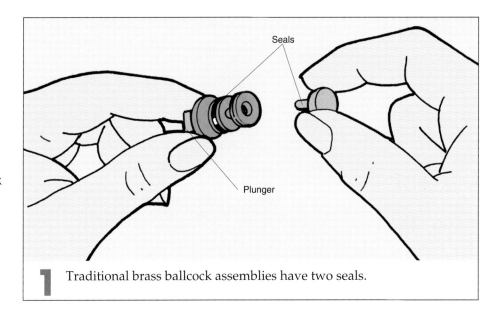

1 Traditional brass ballcock assemblies have two seals.

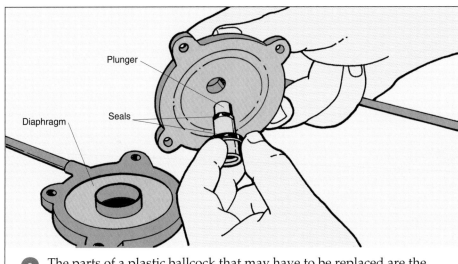

2 The parts of a plastic ballcock that may have to be replaced are the seals and diaphragm.

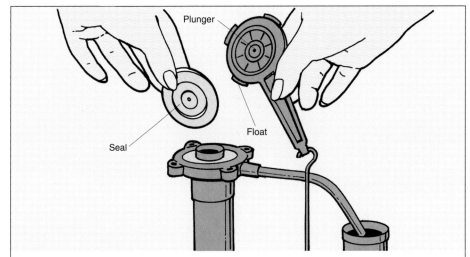

3 The seal inside the plunger of an assembly that has the float as part of the ballcock is the component that has to be replaced.

Ballcock Assembly

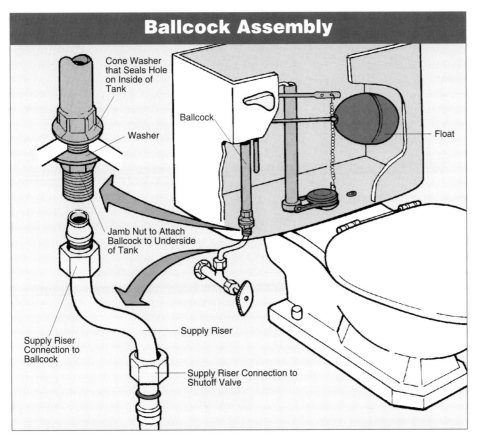

Cone Washer that Seals Hole on Inside of Tank

Washer

Ballcock

Float

Jamb Nut to Attach Ballcock to Underside of Tank

Supply Riser Connection to Ballcock

Supply Riser

Supply Riser Connection to Shutoff Valve

Float Rod & Refill Hose

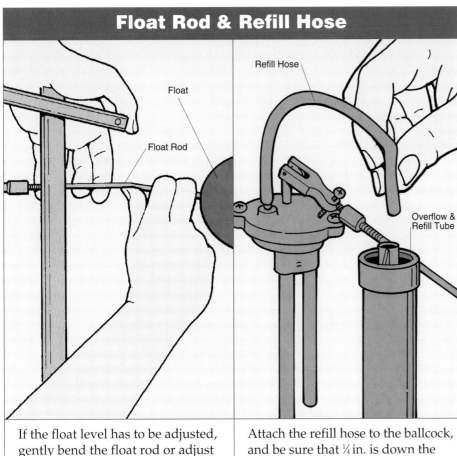

Float

Float Rod

Refill Hose

Overflow & Refill Tube

If the float level has to be adjusted, gently bend the float rod or adjust the screws on the ballcock.

Attach the refill hose to the ballcock, and be sure that ¼ in. is down the throat of the overflow tube.

Replacing a Ballcock

Purchase an antisiphon ballcock to comply with your local plumbing codes. Follow these steps to replace a ballcock:

1 Disassembling Old Ballcock. With the water shutoff valve closed, flush the toilet, and use a sponge to sop excess water from the tank.

Unscrew the float and float rod from the ballcock.

Using an adjustable wrench, remove the riser's coupling nut.

Using adjustable pliers or a pipe wrench, loosen and remove the jamb nut and washer holding the ballcock to the underside of the tank.

2 Installing New Ballcock. Lift the old ballcock out of the tank. Before you install a new metal ballcock in the hole in the base of the tank, spread pipe joint compound around the threads that fit through the hole. If the new ballcock is plastic, use Teflon paste compound around the threads. Install the new ballcock.

Caution: *Do not overtighten connections. When you turn on the water, check for leaks. If there is a leak, tighten that connection a little at a time until the leak stops.*

3 Adjusting Float and Hose. You may have to adjust the float when you attach the float and rod to the ballcock. Water should lie about ¾ of an inch below the top of the overflow tube. Carefully bend the middle of the float rod down a little to lower the float, or bend the rod up to raise the float. Check the result. Proceed in this way until the water rises to the proper level vis-a-vis the overflow tube.

See that the refill hose is attached to the ballcock and that ¼ inch or so is down the throat of the overflow tube.

Tank Does Not Empty Completely

The cause of this problem is often confined to toilets with chain-lifted flapper flush valves. The chain probably has too much slack, restricting the height of the flapper as you activate the handle. The pressure of water on the flapper flush valve causes it to reseat itself before the normal amount of water in the tank can empty, unless you keep the flapper off the valve seat by holding on to the handle.

The thin metal hook that attaches the end of the chain to the trip lever may have stretched a bit. Unhook the chain, and reattach while shortening the chain (near right).

If this does not resolve the problem, the flapper flush valve may have deteriorated, so replace the valve and the chain (far right).

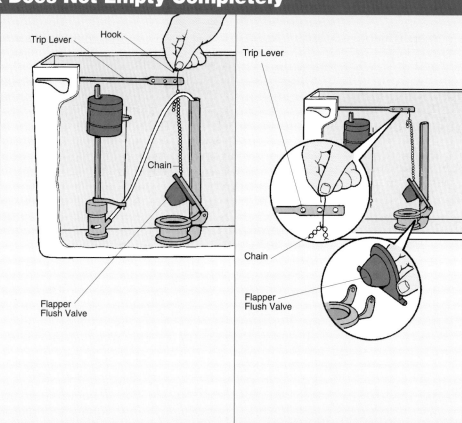

Sluggish Flow of Water into Bowl

If you must flush the toilet more than once to empty the bowl, it is often due to partially blocked flush holes around the rim or a blocked siphon jet hole. By holding a pocket mirror under the rim (near right), check to see if mineral deposits are clogging the flush holes. To clean the holes, straighten a wire coat hanger and carefully poke the end of it into each flush hole to clear deposits, but be careful not to damage the porcelain. Repeat this process with the siphon jet hole (far right). Buy mineral-dissolving compound (hard water stain cleaner) and mix according to directions. Bail water from the bowl to below the siphon jet hole. Remove the tank lid, insert a funnel into the overflow tube, and pour the solution down that tube. After one hour, flush the toilet several times.

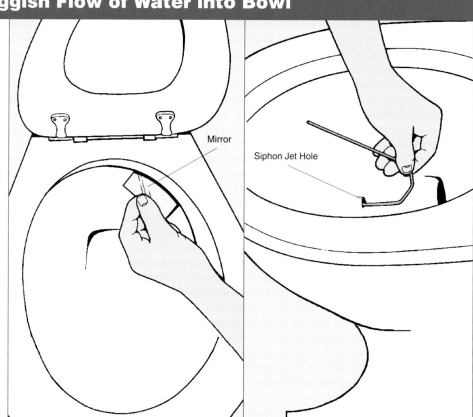

Repairing a Leak from Water-Supply Riser

If there is a drip of water from around one of the nuts that attaches the water-supply riser to the water shutoff valve and ballcock, tighten the nut using an adjustable wrench. If the leak persists with the water shutoff valve closed, loosen the nut and wrap Teflon tape or spread pipe joint compound around the

compression ring and/or around the female threads. Tighten the nut.

If the water-supply riser has sprung a leak, replace it. The job is done the same way as replacing a faucet water-supply riser (page 27). Braided stainless-steel water-supply riser is easier to work with than one made of chromed copper.

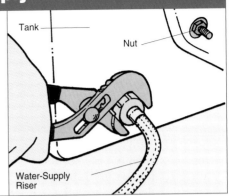

Tank

Nut

Water-Supply Riser

Repairing a Leak from Water-Inlet Pipe Gasket

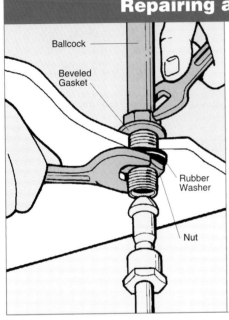

Ballcock

Beveled Gasket

Rubber Washer

Nut

With the water shutoff valve closed, flush the toilet, and remove the tank lid. Using a sponge, sop up the water remaining in the bottom of the tank.

Loosen and unscrew the nuts holding the water-supply riser. Remove the water-supply riser.

Hold or have a helper hold the ballcock. Working beneath the tank, loosen the nut holding the ballcock to the tank. Then remove the nut and gasket. Take these to a plumbing-supply store or home center and get replacements.

Install the new ballcock nut and gasket. Tighten the nut with your

fingers. Then, holding the ballcock, tighten the nut snugly. Overtightening the nut can crack the tank.

Apply Teflon tape (on plastic parts) or spread pipe joint compound (on metal parts) around the compression rings and/or female threads of the water-supply riser, and tighten (but do not overtighten) the nuts.

Turn on the water, and check for leaks around each connection. If there is a drip from any connection, tighten that connection a little at a time until the drip stops.

Repairing a Leak from Tank Mounting Bolts

1. From beneath the tank, tighten the nut. Do not ram it, you can crack the bowl or tank. If drip persists, shut off water; flush toilet; and sop up remaining water in tank.

2. Hold the nut steady with a wrench from under the tank as you unscrew the hold-down bolt inside the tank. Remove the bolt, nut, and washer. Replace with identical parts.

3. Install the new fasteners, but be sure you do not tighten the fasteners excessively. You can crack the tank or bowl.

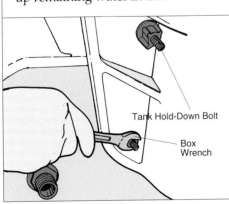

Tank Hold-Down Bolt

Box Wrench

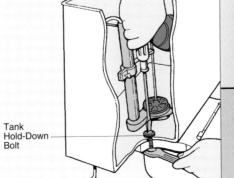

Tank Hold-Down Bolt

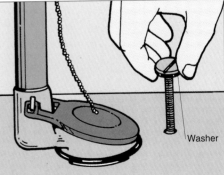

Washer

Repairing a Leak from the Floor Seal

If there is a leak between the bowl and floor, do the following:

1 Removing Mounting Bolts. Remove the caps over the closet bolts. If necessary, pry them off. Loosen and remove the nuts holding the bowl to the mounting bolts and, thus, to the floor. If nuts and bolts are corroded in place, use penetrating oil. If this does not work, cut bolts with a hacksaw.

2 Removing Old Seal. Rock the bowl back and forth to break it free from the wax seal. Then lift the bowl off the floor and place it aside. Stuff a rag into the closet drain opening to prevent sewer gases from permeating the room.

Use a putty knife to remove the old wax seal from the flange of the closet drain and to remove old putty stuck to the floor. If bolts are corroded or had to be cut, slide them off the flange. Scrape residue of old seal and putty off the bottom of bowl. This can get messy, so you may want to have old newspaper to hold the wax as you remove it.

3 Installing New Seal. Slide new mounting bolts into position on the closet flange. Notice that the flange has a wide opening on each end of the slots to let you insert the wide ends of bolts. Center the new wax seal over the opening in the flange, and press the seal into place on the toilet horn.

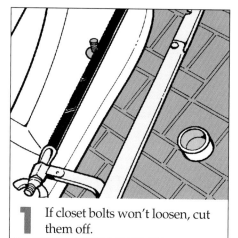

1 If closet bolts won't loosen, cut them off.

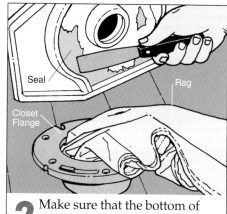

2 Make sure that the bottom of the bowl and the floor are clean.

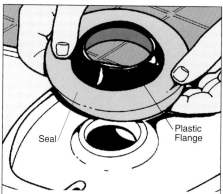

3 Center the new seal over the drain hole in the bowl.

4 Place the toilet onto the flange, and secure the hardware.

4 Attaching the Toilet. Lift the bowl into position over the closet flange, and bring it down to the floor so the mounting bolts protrude through the bolt holes in the bowl flange. Press the bowl down onto the wax seal. Attach cap support washers and nuts. Tighten nuts by hand. Then use a wrench to secure nuts, but do not overtighten or you may crack the bowl. Install caps.

If this is a two-piece toilet, install the tank. Connect the water-supply line. Use plumber's putty or Teflon tape on threads to prevent a leak. Teflon tape must be used on plastic parts. Turn on water, and check for leaks.

Apply a bead of plumber's putty or silicone caulking compound around the perimeter of the bowl base.

Preventing Condensation

Condensation on the sides of a tank occurs when air in the room is warm and humidity is high. The warm air against the cool sides of the tank condenses. Take the following steps to eliminate it:

1. With the water shutoff valve closed, flush the toilet, remove the lid, and sop up water remaining in the bottom of the tank.

2. Using rags, thoroughly dry the sides and bottom of the tank.

3. Turn on the air conditioner or open the window and allow the toilet to remain dormant with the tank lid off for 24 hours.

4. Buy a toilet-tank insulation kit. Cut the foam liners to size; apply adhesive as directed; and install the liners.

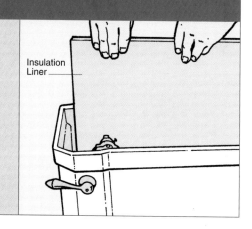

tubs & showers

Anatomy of a Bathtub & Shower

Bathtubs come in several materials, sizes, and styles. They come with showers, which are also available separate from bathtubs in their own stalls. But that is not all there is to bathtub/shower combinations and shower stalls. They are precisely engineered units.

Makeup of a Bathtub

The waste outlet should be 1¹/₂ inches in diameter. The stopper can be a lever-operated pop-up type that when closed seals the waste outlet, a lever-operated metal plunger that when closed seals the waste pipe, or a rubber or metal plug that is inserted into the waste outlet by hand.

Bathtubs have overflows just as most lavatories have overflows. The purpose is to give excess water in the tub an outlet to the waste pipe. The overflow is a hole at least 1¹/₂ inches in diameter that is usually on the faucet side of the tub. It is covered by a plate.

Pop-Up Stopper. If the tub is equipped with a lever-controlled pop-up or plunger stopper, the lever controlling the stopper projects from this plate. To adjust a pop-up stopper, turn the "turnbuckle-type" fitting with pliers and reseat in overflow and drainpipe. Adjust the rod until the stopper fits perfectly.

Joint Sealants. The joints between the tub and the adjoining wall and floor are worthy of mention to remind you of a necessary maintenance task. Most regional plumbing codes consider large spaces between fixtures and walls or floors to be unsanitary because they may collect dirt or provide shelter for vermin. They can also provide a pathway for water to reach the framing behind walls, which can lead to extensive damage.

Thus, if old sealant between the wall and bathtub or floor and bathtub ever falls apart on you, it should be

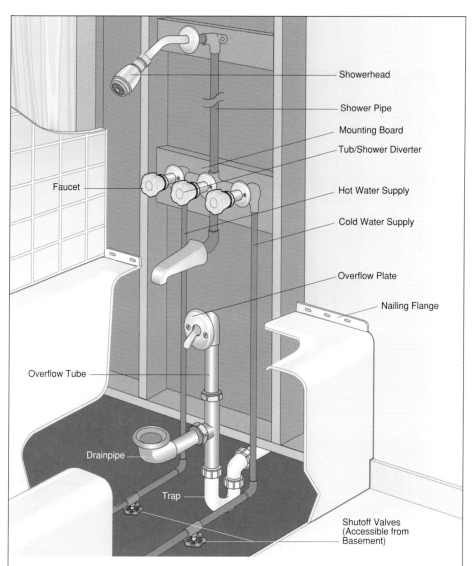

Bathtub & Shower. A typical bathtub arrangement may have water shutoff valves on pipes in the basement that lead to faucets. If there aren't any, water can be turned off by means of the house's main water valve.

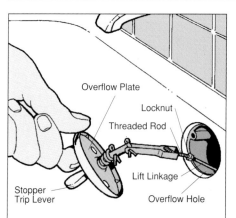

Pop-Up Stopper. To adjust a stopper, turn the "turnbuckle-type" fitting with pliers and reseat in the overflow hole and drainpipe. Adjust the rod so the stopper fits perfectly.

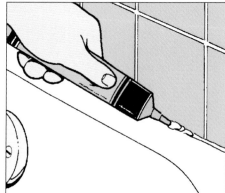

Joint Sealants. If the joint between a bathtub and wall or bathtub and floor has to be renewed, prepare the surface and use a long-lasting, quality caulk.

renewed by removing the crumbled material and applying new sealant. Silicone sealants—available in hardware and home-center stores— are designed for this purpose and will maintain their effectiveness indefinitely.

Makeup of a Shower Stall

Where a shower is by itself in a stall, most regional plumbing codes require that the floor of the compartment be sloped ¼ inch per foot toward the waste outlet. Furthermore, the waste outlet should be 2 inches in diameter and equipped with a strainer to stop hair and keep it from getting into the waste pipe and trap.

You should be able to remove the strainer for cleaning. Therefore, it can either be fastened to the floor with screws or snapped into the outlet opening so it can be turned or pried free from the drain inlet.

There is another detail about shower stall construction to note. The area beneath the floor—which is usually ceramic tile or fiberglass—should be made of a watertight, durable material. This sub-area is called the pan.

The pan should cover the entire base under the floor and extend up on all sides of the stall to a point that is above the stall threshold. Furthermore, the pan should be secured to the waste outlet to make a watertight joint between the two.

The most durable pans are built on site and consist of heavy plastic sheeting covered with a mortar base. One-piece acrylic or fiberglass pans are used for retrofit applications. Multipiece shower-pan kits are also available.

Bathtub & Shower Hardware

Although they may look different, the faucets that serve bathtub/shower combinations and shower stalls are, in most instances, internally the same as those used in sinks and lavatories. Bathtub/shower and shower-stall faucets that have two handles—one

for hot water and one for cold water— are compression or cartridge faucets. If there is one handle, the faucet is of a disc, cartridge, or ball design.

Bathtub/shower combinations have a piece of hardware to keep water from going to the tub's spout and divert it to the showerhead. This is called a diverter. It may be a handle between hot- and cold-water handles, making three handles in all. When the diverter handle is turned clockwise, water flows from the spout. When it is turned counterclockwise, water flows out of the showerhead. The handle-type diverter is equipped with the same kind of mechanism as hot- and cold-

water faucets; that is, it is either a compression or cartridge style. You repair it the same as if you were repairing a two-handle compression or cartridge faucet. (See page 19.)

The other type of diverter used by a bathtub/shower combination is a knob and stem assembly projecting from the top of the spout. When you pull up on the assembly, water is diverted from the spout to the showerhead. This is called a lift-gate diverter. The pressure of the water flowing against the valve keeps the valve raised in place. When the water is turned off, the pressure recedes and the valve drops down. If a lift-

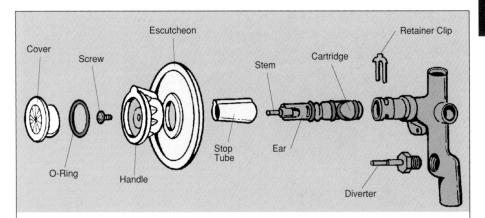

Bathtub-Shower Faucets. Bathtub and shower stall faucets are often of the one-handle, pull-push design. Rotating the handle to the left or right increases the flow of hot or cold water, respectively. This faucet is a one-handle cartridge design.

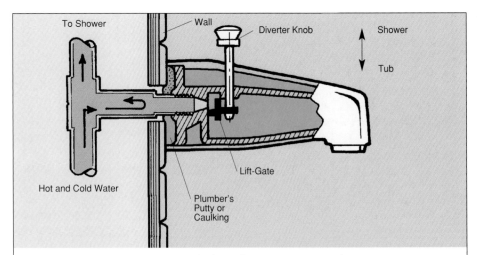

Bathtub-Shower Diverters. When the knob of an in-the-spout diverter is pulled up, the lift-gate blocks the flow of water through the spout and diverts it to the showerhead.

Repairing Two-Handle Faucets & In-the-Wall Diverter

Two-handle faucets that control the flow of hot and cold water from bathtubs and showerheads are of similar design to two-handle faucets that serve sinks and lavatories. They can be compression-style faucets, with washers or diaphragms on the ends of stems, or cartridge-style faucets, with two interacting discs.

The major difference between sink/lavatory and bathtub/shower-stall faucets is that the components of two-handle bathtub/shower stall faucets are larger than those of sink/lavatory faucet assemblies.

When there is a leak from the spout or showerhead of a bathtub/shower stall equipped with two-handle faucets, the faulty component is a stem washer, or stem diaphragm, of a compression-style faucet or the discs of a cartridge-style faucet. You may not know which

one you are dealing with until you have disassembled the faucet.

If there is a handle on the wall between the hot- and cold-water handles, it controls the diverter that switches the flow of water from the spout to the showerhead and vice versa. When this diverter fails, water will come out of the spout and showerhead at the same time, or there will be a trickle of water from the showerhead when the full flow should be from the spout.

The mechanism of the diverter is of the same style as the mechanism of the hot- and cold-water faucets, that is, compression or cartridge. Repair is done the same way as repairing the hot- or cold-water faucets—by replacing the stem washer or diaphragm, or servicing the cartridge.

Disassembly

1 Draining Water. With the water turned off, open the faucet to let water drain.

2 Removing the Cap. If there is a cap in the center of the handle, pry it off by inserting the tip of a screwdriver or putty knife into the ridge between the cap and handle.

3 Removing the Handle. Remove the screw and then the handle. If the handle sticks, tap it lightly with the handle of the screwdriver and wiggle it back and forth until it comes off.

4 Removing the Escutcheon. A decorative plate, called an escutcheon, covers the hole in the wall in which the stem or cartridge sits. Some escutcheons are press fit; others are threaded to mate the adjoining valve. If you cannot remove this plate by hand, wrap adhesive or electrical tape around the jaws of adjustable pliers, grasp the plate with the pliers, and turn it until it comes off. There may or may not be a part called a spacer under the escutcheon. If there is, take it off.

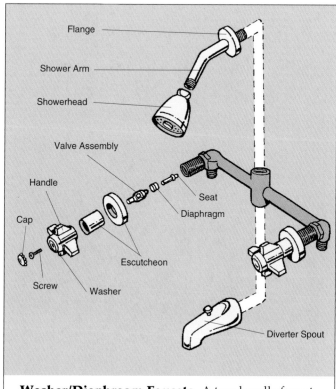

Washer/Diaphragm Faucets. A two-handle faucet may be a compression design with a replaceable washer or diaphragm. Some also have replaceable seats.

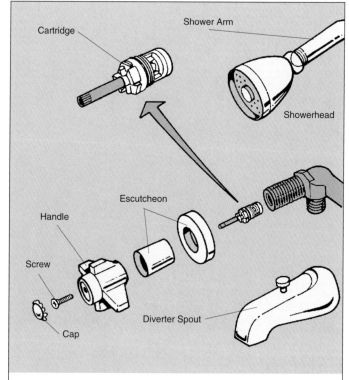

Cartridge Faucets. A two-handle faucet may be of a cartridge design. Cleaning usually does not help and the cartridge must be replaced.

Repair

1 **Removing Stem or Cartridge.** You are now ready to remove the stem or cartridge. Most likely, there will be a six-sided brass nut that needs to be removed. If you can grab it with an adjustable wrench or adjustable pliers, turn it counter-clockwise and remove it. If not, use a ratchet wrench and a socket to remove it. Then, unscrew or pull the stem or cartridge from place.

2 **Replacing Parts.** If this is a compression faucet, undo the brass screw holding the washer to the stem and remove the washer. Take the stem and seat to a plumbing-supply or home-center store, and buy a new washer of the same size and a new brass screw.

If a compression faucet does not have a stem washer, it has a cap called a diaphragm on the bottom of the stem. Pull it off, and buy a new one that is identical.

If the faucet is a cartridge design, open the serrated spokes of the disks and use compressed air to blow dirt from between the spokes. Reassemble the faucet to determine if this action resolves the problem. If it does not, replace the cartridge.

3 **Servicing the Washer Seat.** If this is a compression faucet, service the washer seat before reassembling the faucet. Hold a valve-seat dressing tool against the seat. Using moderate pressure, turn the tool through two revolutions. Then, fill an ear syringe with water and flush out deposits. This action will eliminate burrs or other defects on the seat that could damage the new washer. Use a wire brush to clean deposits from metal parts.

4 **Reassembling the Faucet.** For specific details concerning the repair and assembly of compression and cartridge-style two-handle faucets, see pages 12–13 and 19.

Removing the Stem or Cartridge

1. After undoing the handle, spacer, and escutcheon, the faucet bonnet nut is revealed. Put on eye protection, and chip away any mortar blocking the nut.

2. Use an open-end or adjustable wrench to remove the nut completely, thereby releasing the stem.

3. A tool similar to this one is available for removing a deep-set stem or cartridge.

4. If the faucet has a washer or diaphragm, replace it as you would on a sink or lavatory faucet.

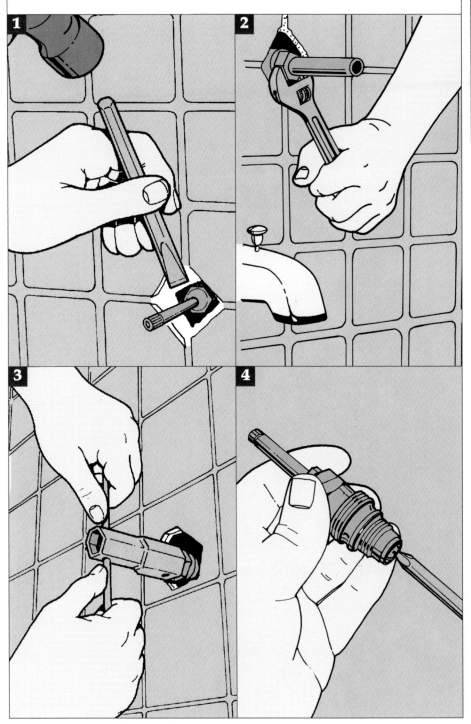

Repairing One-Handle Faucets

A one-handle faucet controls the flow of both hot and cold water to a bathtub spout or shower stall head. As with a one-handle faucet of sinks, this faucet is either a cartridge, disc, or ball design.

Cartridge-Style

1 Removing the Handle. Remove the cap covering the handle screw, and then remove the screw and handle. If the escutcheon is held by a screw, unscrew it to remove the piece.

2 Shutting off the Water. You may see slotted nuts on each side of the faucet control. These are the hot-water and cold-water shutoff valves. Insert a screwdriver into the slot and turn clockwise to shutoff the flow of water on each side. If shutoff valves are not present, turn off the water at the main water valve.

3 Removing the Retaining Ring. There may be a length of tube called a stop tube over the faucet stem. If there is, pull it off. Determine whether there is a threaded retaining ring in place over a cartridge faucet. If so, grasp the ring and turn it counter-clockwise to remove it.

4 Removing the Cartridge. Use pliers to grab the end of the cartridge and pull it out of the wall.

5 Removing the Cartridge Clip. If there is no retaining ring or the cartridge will not come free, examine the housing that holds the cartridge. If you see a clip, pry it from its seat. Then pull the cartridge free.

6 Replacing the Cartridge. Bring the cartridge to a plumbing-supply or home-center store to determine if there are replacement seals, but do not be surprised if you are advised to replace the cartridge: it may be easier than replacing the seals.

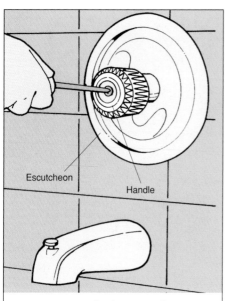

1 Remove the handle, then the escutcheon. Sometimes a hidden screw holds this escutcheon in place.

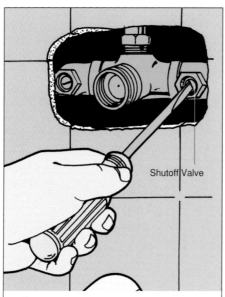

2 Turn off the water by closing the built-in shutoff valves if they are present. If not, turn off the home's main water valve.

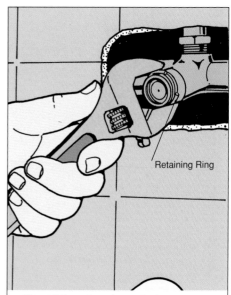

3 If there's a threaded retaining ring over a cartridge faucet, grasp it with an adjustable wrench and turn counterclockwise.

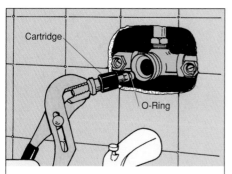

4 Use pliers to grab the end of the cartridge and pull it out of the wall.

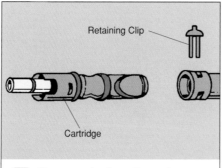

5 Remove the handle and space tube, then pull out the retaining clip to release cartridge.

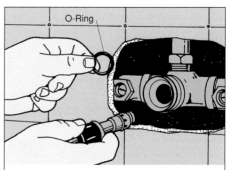

6 Remove the O-ring from the cartridge, and replace it with a new O-ring.

Ceramic Cartridge Faucet Control

Gasket   Stop Tube   Retaining Clip

Cap   Screw   Handle   Cartridge

This bathtub faucet uses a cartridge. If the faucet starts to leak and the spout drips, remove the screws and retaining clip to release the cartridge to replace the O-ring.

Ball-Type Noncompression Faucet Control

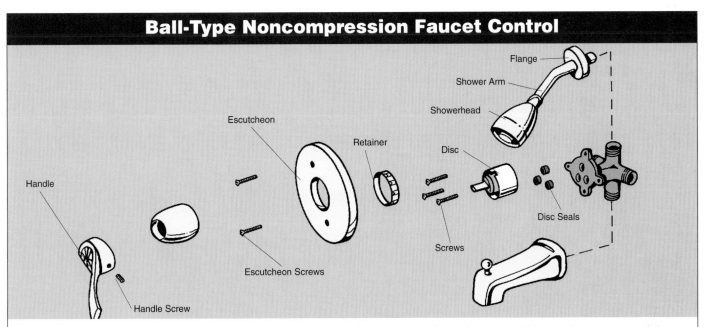

Flange
Shower Arm
Showerhead
Escutcheon
Retainer   Disc
Handle
Disc Seals
Escutcheon Screws   Screws
Handle Screw

Once handle and escutcheon are removed, a disc-style one-handle bathtub or shower-stall faucet is taken out of the wall by removing the screws holding the disc. To repair the leaky faucet, replace the seals in the base of the disc. These seals are usually available in a kit.

Ball-Type Noncompression Faucet Control

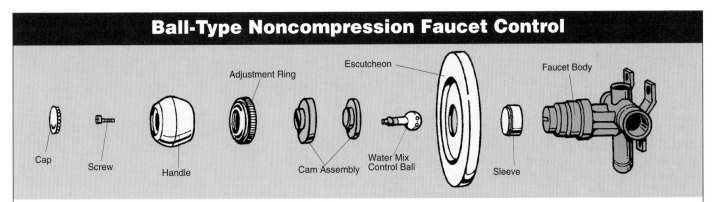

Escutcheon   Faucet Body
Adjustment Ring
Water Mix
Control Ball
Cap   Screw   Handle   Cam Assembly   Sleeve

As for a ball-type noncompression faucet, the same advice offered in the section on dealing with a ball-type faucet of a sink or lavatory (page 16) applies to bathtub and shower-stall faucets. The ball-type noncompression faucet of a tub or shower stall is disassembled in the same way as a ball-type noncompression faucet of a sink or lavatory (after the handle and escutcheon are removed). Replace all parts of the faucet.

Replacing an In-the-Spout Diverter

Is the diverter characterized by a knob and stem on top of the bathtub spout (below left), or by a handle on the wall (below right)? If so, the type you are dealing with is an in-the-spout diverter.

If this part fails, water will come out of the spout as well as the showerhead when it should be coming out of the showerhead alone. Or, the diverter will not stay in the raised position.

Repairing an in-the-spout diverter requires that you replace the spout.

This is a relatively easy procedure as the spout is often simply screwed to the end of the supply pipe. Or the spout is held in place by an Allen screw.

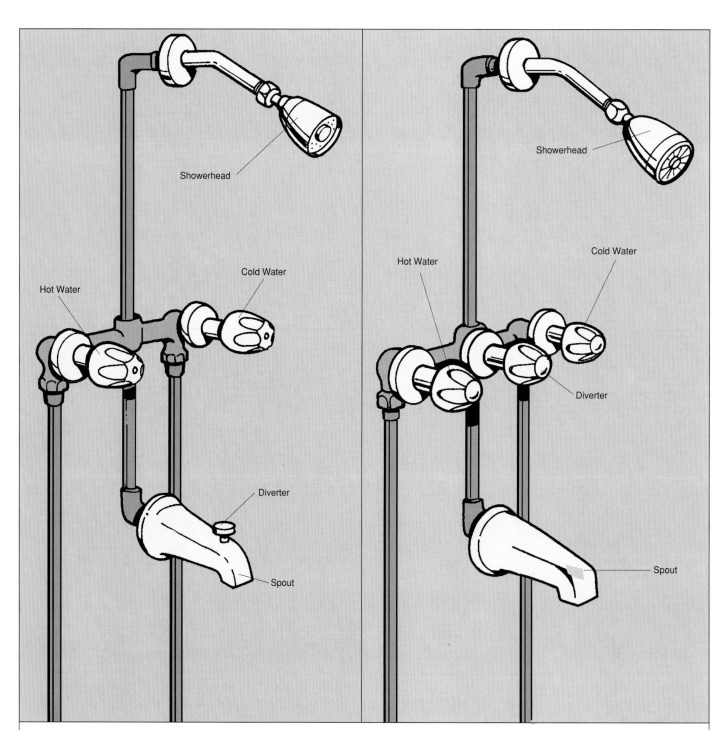

Bathtub-Shower Diverters. The diverter mechanism is either a part of the spout (left) or is located on the wall between the hot and cold water faucets (right). The information in this section concerns in-the-spout diverters. For guidance on how to repair a wall diverter, see pages 42–43.

1 **Removing the Retaining Screw.** Check the underside of the bathtub spout. If a notch is present, the spout is held in place by an Allen screw. Insert different size Allen wrenches until you find the one that fits the screw. Remove the screw and pull the spout free from the pipe.

2 **Removing the Spout.** If the spout is stuck, turn it off by using a screw-driver or the handle of a hammer. Slide the new spout onto the pipe.

If the underside of the spout is a solid case with no notch, then the spout is screwed directly onto the water pipe. Insert the end of a large screwdriver or the handle of a hammer into the spout hole and turn counterclockwise. The spout will come free from the threads of the pipe.

Take the old spout to a plumbing-supply or home-center store to make sure the replacement you get is of the same size. If the spout is threaded, for instance, the set-back distance of the threads inside the new spout have to match the length of the water pipe protruding from the wall.

3 **Installing New Spout.** Wrap pipe-sealing tape clockwise around the threads of the pipe, and screw the new spout onto the pipe.

If the spout hole lies off-center when the spout becomes too tight to turn by hand, insert the screwdriver or hammer handle, and turn it slowly until the hole is pointing down.

Using plumber's putty or silicone caulk, seal the pipe at the point that it enters the wall. Apply the seal to the spout at the top, the back end, and along the sides. This step is done to prevent any water cascading down the wall from finding its way behind the wall.

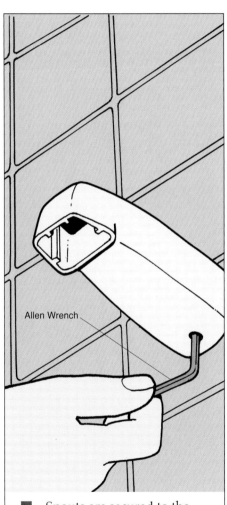

1 Spouts are secured to the wall with an Allen screw, as shown, or are screwed onto the water pipe.

Allen Wrench

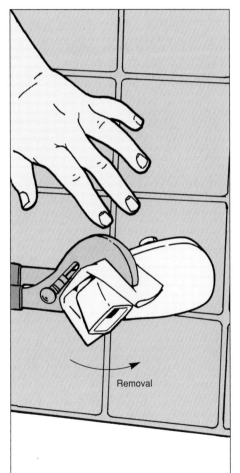

Removal

2 If the spout is screwed to the water pipe, loosen it using a screwdriver or handle of a hammer; then unscrew it with a wrench.

3 Before installing a new spout, wrap pipe-sealing tape around the threads clockwise.

Cleaning a Showerhead

If your showerhead gives forth an uneven spray, you can solve the problem easily.

Removing the Showerhead

Wrap adhesive tape or electrical tape around the showerhead's retainer, or around the jaws of the adjustable wrench or adjustable pliers that you are using to remove the showerhead.

Engage the retainer with the tool and turn counterclockwise (Figure 1) to free the showerhead from the shower arm.

Note: If spray holes are eaten away by corrosion and you want to replace the showerhead, take the old part with you to the plumbing supply or home-center store to make sure the retainer end of the new showerhead is the same as the retainer of the old showerhead.

Cleaning the Showerhead

An uneven spray is caused by sediment settling in and clogging the spray holes. Use an awl or the end of a straightened paper clip to probe deposits from the holes (Figure 2).

There is probably a flow restrictor over the inlet side of the showerhead. Remove any retaining device holding the flow restrictor, and clean the holes from the backside (Figure 3). Flush with water.

If holes are badly plugged, fill a receptacle (large enough to hold the showerhead) with vinegar. Remove the O-ring on the inlet end of the showerhead. Place the showerhead in the vinegar, which may dissolve the deposits. Allow it to soak for several hours. Then, remove the showerhead from the vinegar, and flush it with water.

Reinstalling the Showerhead

Reinsert the O-ring and flow restrictor, and screw the showerhead back onto the shower arm. When you can no longer tighten the showerhead by hand, turn the retainer about one-half turn with the wrench or adjustable pliers. Turn on the water, and check for leaks. If water trickles from around the retainer, tighten it until the trickle ceases.

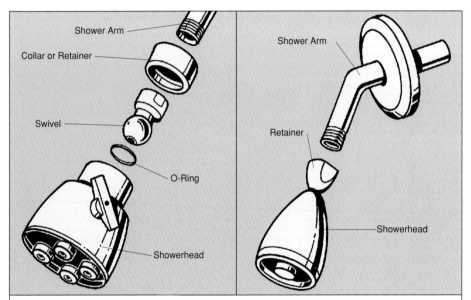

Showerhead Designs. Shown are the parts of the two most common showerhead designs.

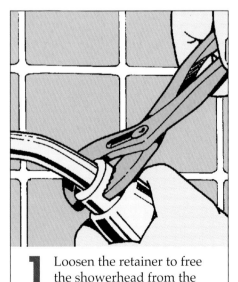

1 Loosen the retainer to free the showerhead from the shower arm.

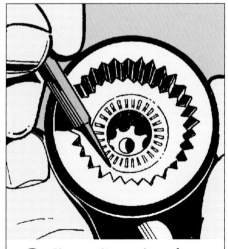

2 Clean sediment from the spray holes in the showerhead.

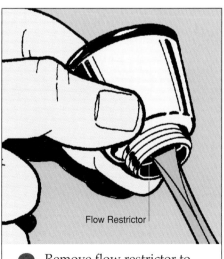

3 Remove flow restrictor to clean sediment in holes in rear of the showerhead.

Repairing Drain Stoppers

When a lever-controlled bathtub drain stopper (called a tripwaste) works well, it is more convenient than a stopper that you manually insert and remove each time you bathe. If a repair is necessary, it is a lot easier to do than it seems.

Identifying the Problem

A tripwaste can malfunction in two ways:

■ The stopper will not seal the waste outlet and water will leak from the bathtub.

■ Water drainage from the tub will become unusually sluggish.

Identifying the Mechanism

There are two types of tripwastes: plunger and pop-up. The plunger is characterized by a strainer cover inserted into the waste outlet. The pop-up drops into or lifts off the waste outlet. Both are controlled by a lever located on the overflow cover.

Plunger Stoppers

1. This tripwaste is an all-in-one assembly made up of the trip lever, linkage, and a plunger on the end of the linkage. The plunger resembles a weight. When you flip the trip lever to seal the waste outlet, the plunger drops into the waste pipe to close the pipe and keep water from flowing out of the tub.

2. If the problem is sluggish drainage, unscrew and clean the strainer before disassembling the tripwaste.

3. To remove the tripwaste mechanism, undo the screws holding the cover plate over the overflow, and pull the cover plate away from the tub. The tripwaste assembly will come out of the overflow. If the problem has been sluggish drainage and cleaning the strainer does not help, the tripwaste mechanism may be clogged with hair. Or you may need to shorten the lift wire.

4. If the problem has been that water leaks from the tub, lengthen the linkage so the plunger will drop further into the waste pipe. Loosen the lock-nut securing the linkage, and screw the rod down about ³⁄₁₆ inch. Check the result. To reinstall a plunger tripwaste back into the overflow, you may have to maneuver the mechanism around a bit to get the plunger to fall into the waste pipe.

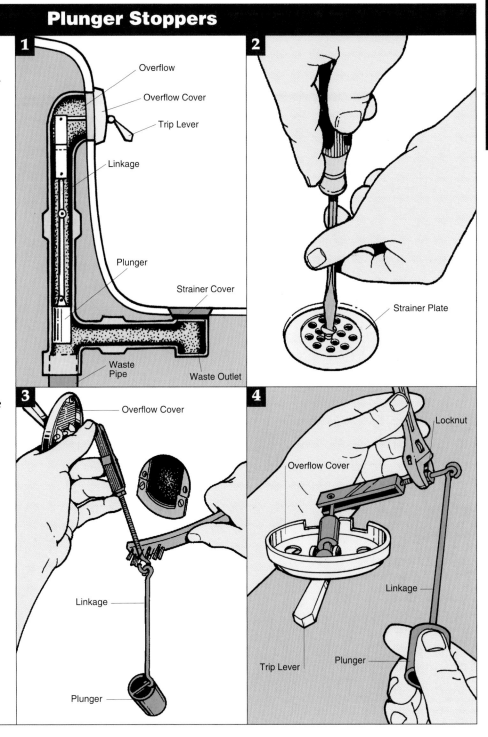

Overflow
Overflow Cover
Trip Lever
Linkage
Plunger
Strainer Cover
Waste Pipe
Waste Outlet
Strainer Plate
Overflow Cover
Linkage
Plunger
Locknut
Overflow Cover
Linkage
Trip Lever
Plunger

Pop-Up Stoppers

1. When the trip lever of a pop-up tripwaste is moved up or down, a coil on the end of a linkage presses down against or releases itself from a rocker arm that is connected to the stopper. This allows the stopper to drop into or lift off the waste outlet.

2. If the problem is a pop-up that allows water to seep away, pull the pop-up from the drain opening. Remove the overflow screws, and pull the tripwaste linkage from the overflow. Lengthen the linkage $\frac{1}{8}$ to $\frac{1}{4}$ inch, and reinstall it. With the tripwaste in the up, or open, position, slide the pop-up back into the drain.

3. If the problem is sluggish draining, remove the stopper/rocker arm assembly; then undo the screws holding the cover over the overflow.

4. Slowly pull the plate away from the bathtub. The trip lever and linkage/coil assembly will come with it.

5. Clean any hair and soap scum from the tripwaste mechanism. If parts are corroded, soak them in vinegar and scrub them with a wire brush.

6. If drainage from the tub is not rapid enough because the stopper does not rise high enough off the waste outlet, adjust the linkage. Loosen the linkage locknut, and turn the threaded end of the linkage so that the linkage is lengthened about $\frac{3}{16}$ inch. Tighten the locknut; reinsert the tripwaste; and check the result.

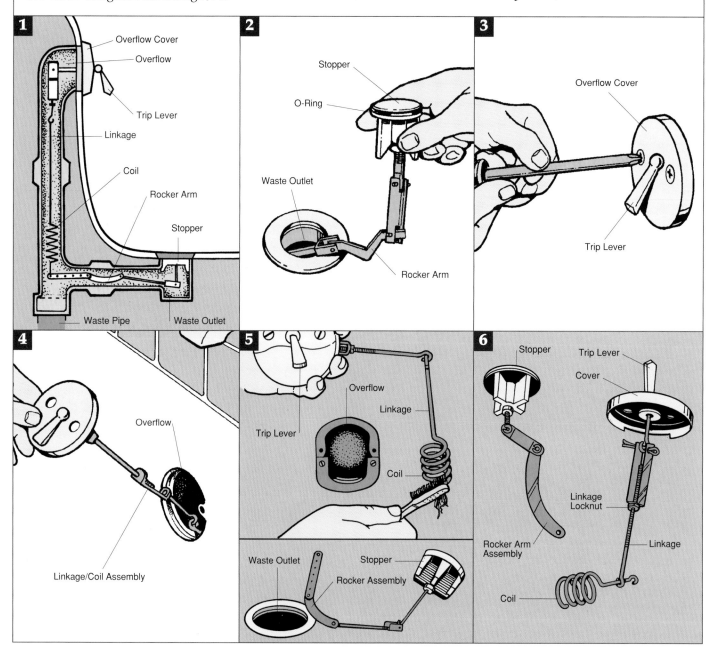

water heaters

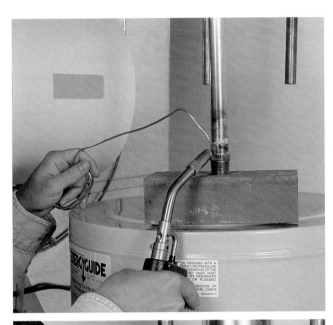

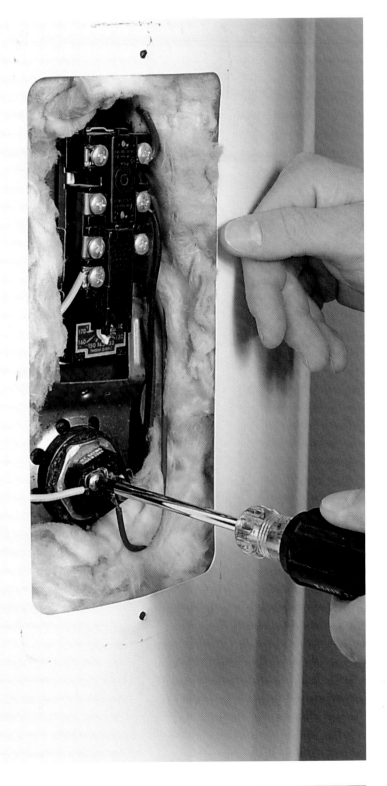

Anatomy of a Water Heater

Water heaters are tanks equipped with energy devices that make water hot. Homes with gas or electric heating systems usually have water heaters with gas burners or electric elements, respectively, to heat water in the tank.

Tankless water heaters don't have storage tanks. They only heat the water that is drawn through them. Long preferred in Europe, they've never really caught on here. They're available in gas or electric, but can have trouble keeping up with demand and cost four or five times as much as a basic gas/electric tank heater.

Making & Delivering Hot Water

When someone turns on a hot water faucet, water flows out the top of the tank through a hot-water pipe. As water leaves the tank, the amount drawn off is replenished through a cold water pipe and an extension of that pipe called a dip tube. The dip tube extends down through the tank with its open end positioned 12 to 18 inches off the floor of the tank.

When a thermostat senses that the temperature of the water in the tank is not at the preset level, the thermostat causes the gas or electric heating unit to turn on. The heating unit stays on and heats the water until the thermostat senses that the temperature of the water has reached the desired level. It then turns the heating unit off.

Other Parts

A water heater has a temperature and pressure (T & P) relief valve and tube assembly to prevent excessive pressure from building up inside the tank and causing an explosion. If the temperature of the water inside the tank exceeds approximately 200°F because a malfunctioning thermostat and a high-limit switch allows the heating source to remain on, the T & P relief valve opens to allow hot water or steam to pour out the relief tube. Pressure inside the tank is reduced to a safe level.

A water heater also has a water drain to allow you to drain the tank. Furthermore, most water heaters are equipped with a magnesium anode (or sacrificial) rod. Its purpose is to attract electrons in the water that would otherwise attack the tank's metal lining, causing it to corrode and leak. Once a tank leaks, it has to be replaced. The anode rod, therefore, extends the life of the tank. The anode can be replaced.

Gas-fired water heaters have a flue to carry deadly carbon monoxide outside the house. Carbon monoxide may be created by natural gas if it does not burn properly.

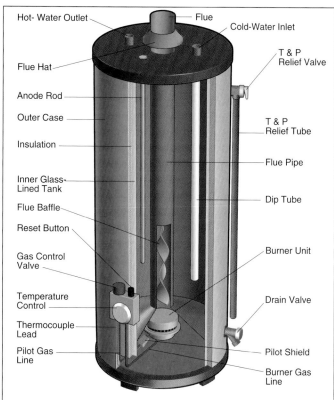

Gas Water Heater. This water heater has a burner at the bottom, much like that on a kitchen range. The flue in the center of the tank routes deadly carbon monoxide (a by-product of burning gas) outside the house.

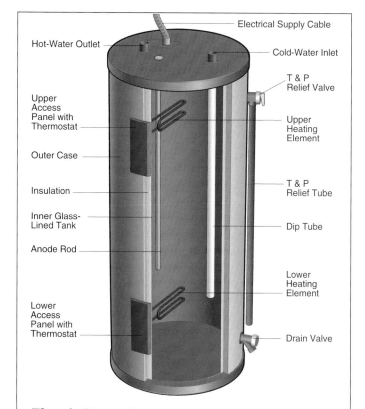

Electric Water Heater. This water heater usually has two heating elements, each with its own thermostat. Smaller tanks (less than 40-gallon tank capacity) may have only one thermostat or heating element.

Heat Generation

Electric water heaters that hold 40 gallons or more usually have two elements that are wired directly to the home's fuse or circuit breaker panel. One element is in the lower part of the tank; the other is in the upper part of the tank. Each element is equipped with its own thermostat. Smaller electric water heaters have one element.

The parts involved in the production of heat in a water heater that uses natural gas include a gas control valve, temperature control dial, and a standing pilot light or spark ignitor. The controls let you turn off gas when a repair is needed or when the house is not going to be occupied for a time.

There are three positions on the burner control: ON, OFF, and PILOT. When set to ON, gas can get to the burner and pilot. The pilot stays lit all the time. The burner comes on when the thermostat senses that water temperature is too low and opens a valve to allow gas to reach the burner.

When the burner control is set to OFF, gas cannot get to the burner or pilot. The pilot is off.

When set to PILOT, gas cannot get to the burner, but it can get to the pilot, which stays lit all the time.

The pilot reset, which is next to the burner control, is used to relight the pilot if you turn the burner control to OFF or the pilot is blown out by a gust of wind. The discussion on page 54 explains how to use this part.

A thermocouple is a safety device that is part of the pilot. It automatically turns off gas flowing to the pilot if the flame goes out because of a gust of wind or a malfunction. Thus, gas will not escape into the house.

If you experience a problem with the gas controls of your water heater other than having to relight a pilot every once in a while, call the gas company serving your area. The gas company is responsible for seeing that gas-handling components perform safely and properly. This service is provided to gas company customers free of charge or at a nominal fee.

Insulating Pipes & Water Heater

If there never seems to be enough hot water, insulating the water heater (below left) and hot-water pipes (below right) may help. Hardware and home-center stores sell several variations of insulation materials. Manufacturers claim insulation saves fuel and therefore reduces the cost of operation.

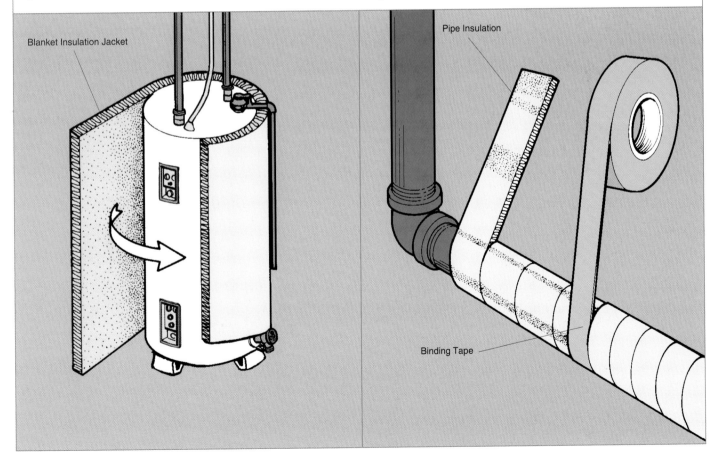

Blanket Insulation Jacket

Pipe Insulation

Binding Tape

Draining the Tank

Draining a pail or two of water from the tank every month can help prevent noise that results when sediment builds up on the tank floor.

Furthermore, to prevent broken pipes and tanks from freezing water, you may have to drain the tank completely if the home is left unoccupied during cold weather.

To drain the tank completely, follow these steps:

1 **Shutting Energy Source.** If it is an electric water heater, remove the fuse or turn off the circuit breaker that protects the circuit. If you are dealing with a gas water heater, turn the temperature (burner) control to OFF, and turn off the gas.

2 **Draining Tank.** Close the shutoff valve on the cold-water pipe. Open all the hot-water faucets in the house and leave them open.

Attach a garden hose to drain the valve and extend the hose to a drain or sump, or outside the house. The hose spout must be lower than the drain valve. Open the drain valve and allow water to drain entirely. This takes some time so be patient.

When the tank has been drained, try to tip it toward the drain valve, but do not exert pressure against the pipes. The purpose is to get as much water as possible out of the tank without causing damage.

3 **Refilling Tank.** To fill the tank again, close the drain valve, and open the valve on the cold-water pipe. When the tank is full, water will flow from the open hot-water faucets.

Turn off the faucets and restore electricity to an electric water heater. If you are dealing with a gas water heater, light the pilot according to directions on the instruction plate on the tank.

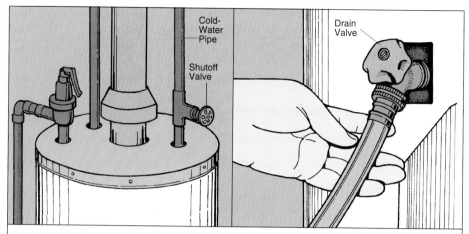

Draining the Tank. To drain a water heater, first close the cold water shutoff valve on the pipe to keep water from flowing into the tank. Then attach a hose to the bib and extend the hose to a drain that is below the level of the bib.

Relighting a Gas Pilot

If you turn the burner control of a gas water heater to OFF, the pilot will go out. A draft also can cause the pilot to flame-out. But if the pilot keeps going out after you relight it, the gas company should be informed.

Follow this procedure to relight a pilot:

1. Turn the burner control to PILOT.

2. Take off both the outside and inside covers over the burner and pilot. Both covers are usually removed by simply lifting them off.

Caution: *If the burner was on just before the pilot light flamed out, the inner cover could be red hot.*

3. Hold a lit match near the pilot and press the pilot reset. It is next to the burner control. The pilot should light. Extinguish the match, but keep your finger pressed down on the pilot reset for 60 seconds.

4. If the flame stays lit, turn the burner control to ON and reinstall the covers.

Setting Temperature

The temperature at which to keep water is the lowest possible setting conducive with satisfactory—and safe—results; usually 120°F.

Raising the temperature does not mean you are going to get a larger supply of hot water. It just means you will get hotter hot water. If water creates steam as it comes out of the faucets, the water is much too hot.

Gas Water Heaters

To set the temperature of water heated by gas to a desired level, hold a calibrated thermometer to record at least 160°F or more under a hot-water faucet for two minutes. Then note the reading.

If it is not to your liking, turn the temperature control dial to the appropriate index mark—clockwise to raise the temperature or counter-clockwise to lower the temperature.

The temperature control dial of a gas water heater is not usually marked numerically in degrees. Each index mark represents about a 10-degree increase or decrease.

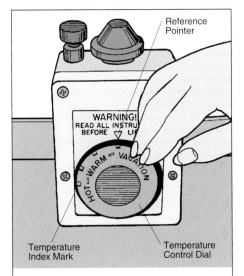

Gas Water Heaters. Set water to the desired temperature by turning the temperature control dial until the desired temperature index mark lines up with the reference pointer. Check water temperature with a thermometer.

Electric Water Heaters

Temperature controls of electric water heaters are usually marked numerically in degrees. These controls, however, are not exposed and therefore are more difficult to get at than a temperature control dial of a gas water heater.

If your water heater has two elements, each has its own temperature control. One or two covers screwed to the tank conceal them. Follow these steps:

Remove the fuse or turn off the circuit breaker protecting the electric circuit serving the water heater.

The screws which hold the cover(s) to the tank should be removed. Then remove the cover(s).

If there is a panel of insulation under the cover(s), remove it. If the insulation is fiberglass, wear gloves to protect your hands and spread apart the insulation to reveal the temperature controls.

Use a screwdriver to turn one temperature control, then the other, to the desired setting. Both should be set at the same temperature.

Replace the insulation and reinstall the cover(s).

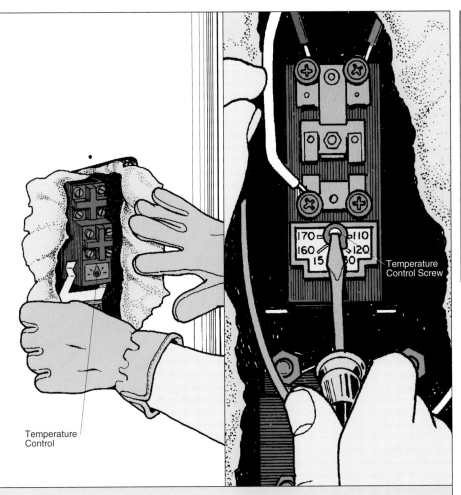

Electric Water Heaters. After turning off the electricity, unscrew the covers from the tank and fold back the insulation to get at the temperature controls (left). Before turning the temperature-dial control screw to the desired number, be sure the power is OFF. The temperature control of an electric water heater is marked numerically in degrees (right).

Repairing:

Temperature & Pressure Relief Valve

The temperature and pressure (T & P) relief valve is the most important safety component on a water heater. This section describes how to know when the valve has malfunctioned and how to install a new one. The valve is located on the side or on the top of the tank.

Replacement

Water dripping from the pipe connected to the T & P relief valve is a sign that the valve is weak and should be replaced. Make sure the water temperature is not too hot because of an improperly set thermostat.

1 Testing the Valve. Test the operation of a T & P relief valve every so often to make sure valve is still operative. Place a pail under the T & P pipe, and lift the valve lever. Water should flow out of the pipe. If not, replace the valve.

With the gas or electricity to the unit turned off, close the shutoff valve of the cold-water pipe. Do not use any faucets. If this is not possible, turn off the main water supply.

2 Removing Valve Pipe. Open the relief valve, and drain the water to the level of the valve. Using a pipe wrench to hold the T & P relief valve, turn the relief pipe out of the valve with another wrench. Loosen the relief valve by turning it counter-clockwise with a pipe wrench.

3 Removing Valve. Wear gloves; the valve may be hot and dirty.

4 Replacing Valve. Buy a new T & P relief valve with the same Btu/hour rating as the water heater. Check the data plate attached to the water heater to find out what it is.

5 Installing Valve. Coat the threads of the new valve with Teflon tape, and screw it into the tank.

6 Installing Valve Pipe. Coat the threads of the relief pipe with Teflon tape. Screw the pipe into the relief valve.

1 Place a pail under the T & P relief pipe, and lift the handle.

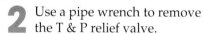

2 Use a pipe wrench to remove the T & P relief valve.

3 Take T & P relief valve out of the tank. Sediment may be on it.

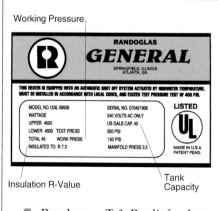

4 Purchase a T & P relief valve that matches the working pressure rating of the tank.

5 Seal the threads, and install the new T & P relief valve.

6 Seal the threads, and attach the T & P relief pipe to the T & P relief valve.

clearing clogs

Clearing Sink Drains

Next to leaking faucets, clogged sink and lavatory drains are probably going to be your biggest plumbing headache. Usually, it is not the fault of the system, but of those using the system. Traps and waste pipes are intended to handle liquid, not solids. Hair, bits of soap, scraps of food, and grease flowing into the system can cause a clog. So can debris put into a sink by a do-it-yourselfer who washes off paint brushes and putty knives.

Traps and waste pipes of kitchen sinks outfitted with food waste disposers can handle ground-up slush. They will not clog as long as slush is washed away with an ample flow of water.

The steps for clearing a clogged sink or lavatory drain should proceed from the easiest to the most difficult to perform. Begin with plunging. If that does not work, use a hand snake.

Chemical drain cleaners are not recommended. Mechanical procedures are usually more effective. However, if you are going to use a chemical drain cleaner, despite the recommendation not to do so, follow the directions on the container carefully, and wear goggles, heavy rubber gloves, and protective clothing.

Note: If you are working on a lavatory drain that is clogged, the first thing to do is to release the pop-up stopper and withdraw the stopper from the drain hole. You might be surprised at the amount of soap scum and hair that has built up on the stem of the stopper. It could be causing slow drainage. Cleaning off this accumulation with paper towels and pipe cleaners may clear the clog. If not, proceed with plunging.

Plunging a Clog

1. Using rags, block all openings that are part of the sink or lavatory setup. This includes overflow holes and the drain hole of the other sink if the clogged sink is part of a double-sink setup.

2. The drain hose of a dishwasher should be closed by placing blocks of wood on its top and bottom surfaces and pressing them together with a C-clamp.

3. Spread a thin layer of petroleum jelly on the rim of the plumber's helper to affect a more perfect seal between the rubber cup and the sink or lavatory.

4. With 2 to 3 inches of water in the basin, place the rubber cup over the drain hole. Use steady, rhythmic, and forceful downward strokes to clear the clog. Try ten strokes at a time; then test the flow of water down the drain. If the drain is clear, let the hot water run for about five minutes to wash away residue left by the clog.

Do not forget to remove rags from openings that you closed off, and the C-clamp and wood blocks from the drain hose of a dishwasher.

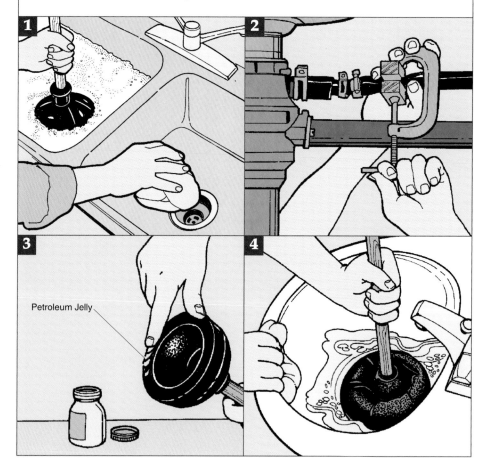

Petroleum Jelly

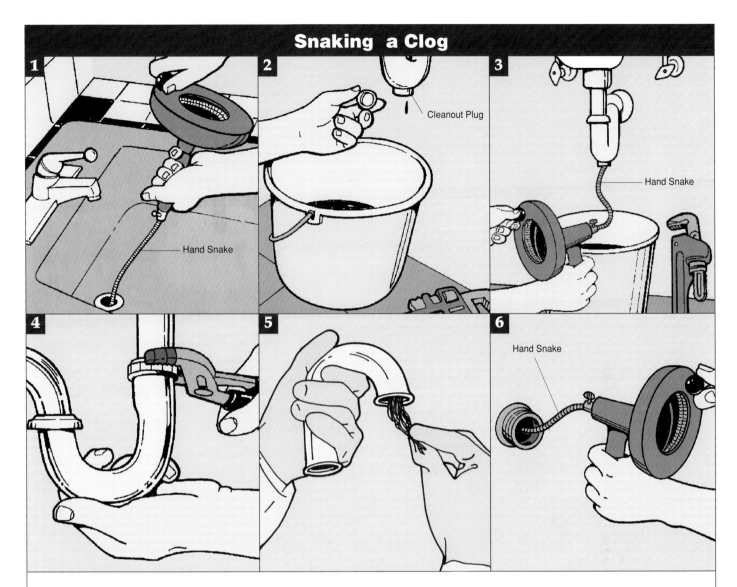

1

2

Cleanout Plug

3

Hand Snake

Hand Snake

4

5

6

Hand Snake

If plunging does not clear the clog after five attempts, it is time for the more drastic measure of snaking. There are several ways to approach this operation.

1. Try clearing the clog by inserting the snake through the drain hole in the sink.

2. If this does not work and the trap has a cleanout plug, loosen and remove the plug. Place a pail under the trap to catch whatever flows out of the cleanout plug.

3. Try to clear the clog by inserting the snake through the hole into the waste pipe. When you reinstall the cleanout plug, wrap a layer of Teflon tape around the threads to prevent a leak.

4. If there is no cleanout plug, use adjustable pliers or a wrench to undo the fasteners holding the trap. Place a pail under the trap.

5. Clean out the trap using a small brush, or you might try forcing a cloth through it.

6. Use a hand snake to clear the waste pipe. If you encounter stiff resistance, withdraw the snake and start again. Most likely, the resistance is caused by the snake hitting against the pipe. Clogs usually are caused by soft material that the snake is able to pass through easily.

Reinstall the trap, and let the hot water flow for about five minutes.

Clearing Clogs

Clearing Stall Shower Drains

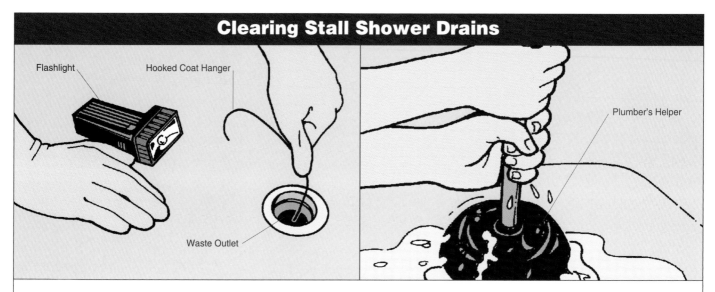

A clog in the drain of a shower stall is most likely hair mixed with soap scum. The part of the drain that receives the brunt is the strainer. Soap-coagulated hair twines itself around the slots, impeding the flow of water.

To regain forceful drainage, remove the strainer by undoing the screws or by twisting the strainer out of the waste outlet if there are no screws. Wearing rubber gloves to protect your hands from the gooey mess, use

paper towels to clean the slots of the strainer. If necessary, use the tip of an awl or screwdriver to break entangled hair free.

Wash the strainer, but before returning it to the waste outlet, turn on the faucet and check the flow down the waste pipe to see if there is a problem other than a clogged strainer.

If water flows freely, return the strainer to the waste outlet. If water backs up, form a hook in one end of a straightened-out wire coat hanger.

Shining a flashlight down the waste pipe to spot wads of hair in the pipe, use the hook to fish the blockage out of the pipe (above left).

Hold the cup of a plumber's helper over the waste outlet; run the water until the cup is covered; and pump the tool up and down vigorously a number of times (above right). This will clear the trap. Finally, flood the drain with plenty of hot water.

Clearing a Bathtub Drain

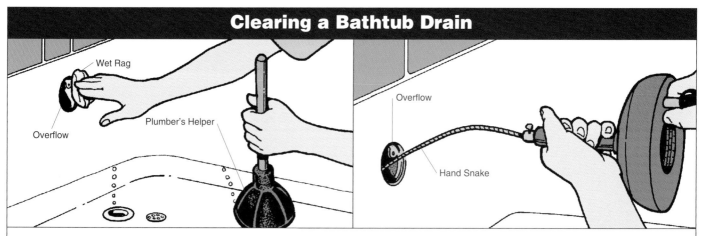

If servicing the tripwaste has no effect on drainage out of the bathtub (page 49), use a plumber's helper. Remove the cover over the overflow, and stuff a cloth into the hole to seal it. Fill the tub so water will cover the cup of the plumber's helper. Now, plant the plumber's helper over the

waste outlet and pump up and down as vigorously as you can. Test the result.

If the flow is now adequate, flood the drain with hot water. But if the stoppage persists, use a hand snake to clear it.

Take off the overflow cover and remove the pop-up or plunger tripwaste assembly. Then insert the snake through the overflow to ream out the waste pipe and trap.

Clearing Toilet Clogs

If the water in a bowl rises to the rim or overflows, it is likely that something is clogging the channel (trap), preventing the water and contents from entering the drain. Usually, the restriction is easily cleared.

First Try

Use an old cup or a tin can to bail water from the bowl.

Place a small mirror at an angle in the drain hole, and shine a flashlight into the mirror so the light beam reflects into the channel for better visibility.

If you can spot the obstruction, try to fish it out using a wire coat hanger that has been straightened out and has a hook at one end.

Plumber's Helper

If the clog cannot be relieved the easy way, use a plumber's helper. The type of plumber's helper you want for a toilet is one that has a flange on the end of the cup. You can clear most toilet bowl stoppages with this tool.

Insert the bulb into the drain, press down, and vigorously pump the handle of the plumber's helper several times. Then flush the toilet to test results.

Caution: Keep your hand on the water shutoff valve in case water begins to rise to the point of overflowing.

Repeat the procedure four or five times before giving up and turning to a closet auger.

Closet Auger

The closet auger is designed to flex around the turns in the channel that form the trap while still being stiff enough to force its way through practically any obstruction. It is a fairly expensive tool so you may want to rent one instead of purchasing.

To use a closet auger, place the working end of the auger into the bowl. Turn the handle to snake the end through the channel. When you hit the obstruction, turn and push harder. Repeat the snaking action several times. Follow by flushing the toilet with the above caution in mind.

Testing Results

To test the results, throw a few feet of toilet paper into the bowl and flush. Keep your hand on the water shutoff valve just in case. If the paper swirls vigorously down the drain, you have succeeded. If not, more plunging or auger action is needed.

Drastic Action

If the obstruction in the trap is so solidly stuck that even a closet auger will not clear it out, detach the bowl from the floor, turn it upside down, and clear the obstruction from the bottom side of the bowl. How to remove a bowl is described on page 38.

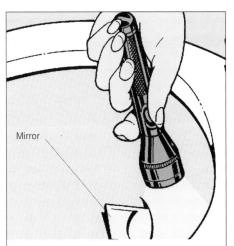

First Try. By using a small mirror and flashlight, you may be able to see an obstruction in the top of the trap. If so, try fishing it out with a wire coat hanger.

Plumber's Helper. A plunger with a flange on the end of the cup provides greater force to clear an obstruction than one without.

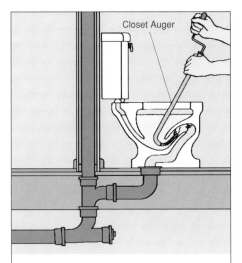

Closet Auger. The auger is flexible enough to make the turns in the trap. Insert the auger and turn the handle.

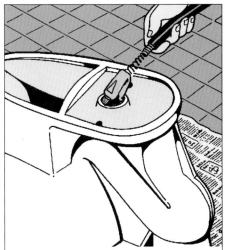

Drastic Action. If you can't clear a clog with a plunger or auger, remove the bowl (see page 38) and tackle the problem from below.

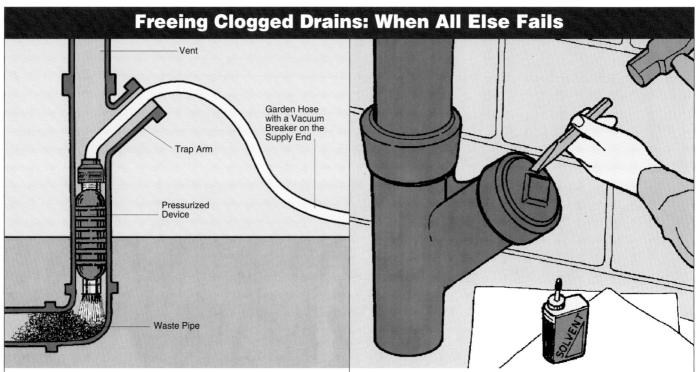

Vent

Trap Arm

Garden Hose with a Vacuum Breaker on the Supply End

Pressurized Device

Waste Pipe

1 It is rare that a clog in a waste pipe will resist plunging and augering. If it does, you might want to try a device that exerts tremendous water pressure against the clog before calling a professional. You can buy or rent one from a plumbing supply dealer.

2 The most serious clog occurs when matter, such as tree roots, invades the lateral pipe leading to the sewer. A professional will probably be needed to deal with this. He will first open the cleanout plug to allow access to the main drain and lateral.

Power Auger

Foot Switch

Power Auger

3 The cutting end of the power auger will be fed into the network through the cleanout.

4 A clog cannot usually withstand the force exerted upon it by the power auger.

pipes

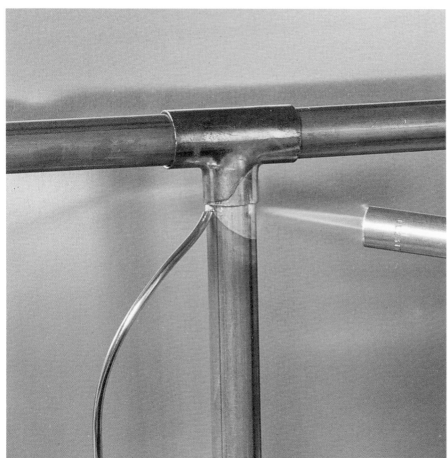

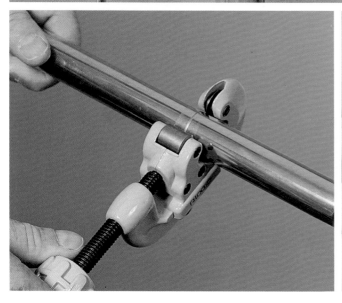

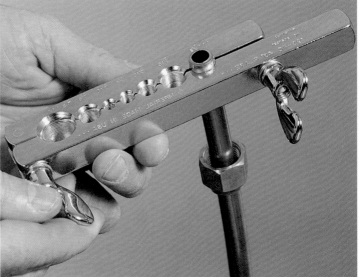

Preventing Frozen Pipes

In an occupied house, there are several ways to keep the temperature of the pipes above the freezing point.

If the basement or crawl space is not heated and therefore may drop below freezing, wrap foam tubing or insulation batts around sections of pipe. Basement sills, crawl spaces, and cantilevered floor joists are primary locations.

You also could install a space heater. An electric, thermostatically controlled unit that hangs from a joist may be most effective; but it is costly.

If water pipes pass through the uninsulated outside walls of the house, heat delivered by the home heating system will not protect them from freezing. In this case, there are four options: (1) during cold snaps, allow water to run from faucets at a low-to-moderate stream; (2) have insulation blown into the outside walls where pipes are located; (3) provide heat from an external source; (4) cut and reroute pipes to take them out of the weather walls.

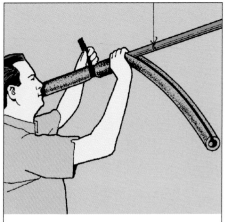

1 Protect pipes from the cold with foam tubing that comes in lengths that have been split.

2 If you have any leftover fiberglass insulation, you can use that instead of foam tubing.

3 Another kind of pipe protector is UL-listed electric heat tape, which is wrapped around the pipe and plugged into an electric outlet.

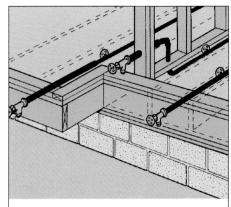

4 Pipes that pass through exterior walls are susceptible to freezing. Pack insulation above the sill as a precaution.

Thawing a Frozen Pipe

A diminished flow of water indicates a frozen pipe that has not burst. Heat the frozen section with a heat gun or hair dryer.

Caution: *Do not touch the pipe while proceeding with this step. Also, be sure the heat gun or hair dryer is plugged into a GFCI outlet.*

Move the heat gun or hair dryer back and forth so the heat is not concentrated in one spot. You will need an assistant to stand over the faucet and monitor the flow of water. When the water flows at a normal rate, the obstacle is cleared.

If you are not sure which section is frozen, feel along the pipes with your hand. Do this gingerly with hot-water pipes. Usually a frozen section will feel colder than the rest of the pipe.

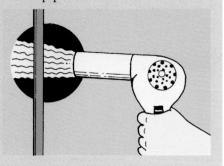

5 Pipes running up an exterior wall may freeze and split. Consider having these walls professionally packed with insulation blown inside the walls.

If the home is not going to be occupied during cold weather, and therefore the heating system will be turned off, the plumbing system should be drained to prevent frozen pipes. Follow these guidelines:

1. The first step in draining a home's water system is to close the main shutoff valve or switch off the submersible pump.

2. If the water heater is electric, remove the fuse in the main electric service panel or flip off the circuit breaker. If the water heater is gas, turn off the main gas valve.

3. Open all faucets and drain valves (including outdoor faucets), and flush all toilets. Use a large sponge or syringe to empty toilet bowls; bail out remaining water.

4. Drain the water heater. If you have a private water system, drain the water holding tank as well as any water treatment equipment.

5. If there is a hot-water heating system, turn off the furnace and open radiant equipment drain valves. Then, drain the furnace.

6. Examine the valves for small circular knobs that contain tiny holes in them. These knobs act as drains. Loosening them while the valve is closed allows trapped water to drain.

7. Antifreeze can be purchased for home use at hardware stores or home-supply outlets. Depending on the lowest temperature anticipated in the home, mix the solution for the appropriate potency level. Pour about 8 ounces into every trap, including all toilet bowls, sinks, showers, bathtubs, and the washing machine standpipe. Traps may be hidden.

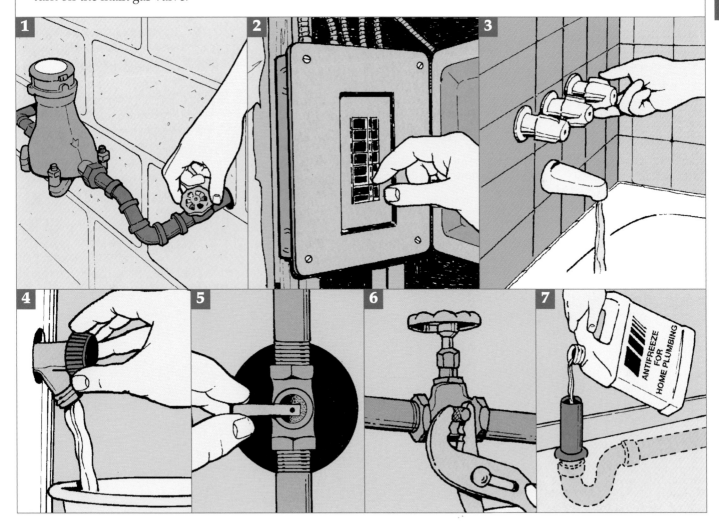

Silencing Noisy Pipes

A loud noise heard after a faucet is shut or the washing machine or dishwasher turns off is most likely caused by water hammer. Depending upon the method that is needed to solve the problem, the job is either easy or difficult. If the sound is caused by a pipe hanger that has come loose, the repair for this problem is easy to do. However, if that is not the case, a more extensive repair may be necessary.

Draining Pipes

Examine water pipes that are exposed, such as those going to the washing machine. Look for extensions on pipes that are capped and rise above or fall below shutoff valves. These are air-cushioning chambers. If the exposed pipes have them, it is an indication that all water delivery pipes in the house have them, so lack of air chambers is not the problem.

Every so often, however, one or more air chambers becomes waterlogged. When this happens, air is no longer present to absorb the shock resulting from the water when the flow is turned off. Alleviate the condition this way:

■ Turn off the home's main water shutoff valve or switch off the submersible pump.

■ Open all faucets and allow the system to drain. Given enough time, water trapped in the air chambers may drain as well.

■ Turn the water back on. Water will fill the water-delivery pipes without filling the air chambers. Realistically, air chambers will become water-logged quickly. If your house is plagued by water hammer, install mechanical shock Arrestors.

Note: Even if all of the water pipes in your home are concealed, and you cannot tell whether or not pipes are outfitted with air chambers, take the time to perform the above procedure.

Cushioning Pipes

If the previously described treatment does not alleviate the noise, assume that the noise is coming from a pipe that is vibrating against a wooden framing member of the house. With water pipes that are exposed, there is little trouble in securing them.

Inspect pipes from one end to the other, looking for those that lie right up against a joist. Place insulation between the pipe and joist. The insulation acts as a cushion.

Check the metal pipes that hang from joists. There may be an insufficient number of hangers or a hanger may have loosened. Hangers used for metal pipes should be made of the same metal as the pipe to prevent a galvanic reaction. The pipe should be held solidly so there is little or no movement. Make sure metal pipes are held by a hanger at every joist.

CPVC water pipe must be treated differently to allow for thermal expansion and contraction. Therefore, see that the CPVC water pipe is supported every 32 inches; that is, to every other joist. Use

special plastic hangers made for CPVC. They allow it to slide back and forth as the temperature inside the pipe changes. Hangers are available at plumbing-supply stores.

Installing Air Chambers

If the above treatments have not resolved the problem, air chambers or shock Arrestors will probably have to be installed into the system. Each hot- and cold-water pipe going to faucets and appliances should be equipped. The task will not be too difficult if pipes are exposed. However, concealed pipes will require the removal of walls.

Note: There are two ways to do this job: (1) Install air chambers as described here (the less expensive way). Air chambers must be a size larger than the pipe. (2) Install shock Arrestors, which are mechanical devices that work by means of pistons or bellows. Shock Arrestors (available at plumbing supply stores) are easier to install, but are more costly. Installation instructions are included.

Cushioning Pipes. Insulation between pipes and wood framing acts as a cushion to reduce noise.

Installing Shock Arrestors

1. Turn off the water; drain the system. Cut copper or CPVC pipe to accept a copper or CPVC T-fitting as close to the faucet or water-intake valve as possible.

2. Solder a copper T-fitting to cut the copper water pipe. Solvent-weld a CPVC T-fitting to the CPVC pipe.

3. Solder a copper nipple or solvent weld a CPVC nipple to the T-fitting.

4. Solder a copper reducer or solvent-weld a CPVC reducer to the nipple. If the water pipe is ½ inch, use a ½-inch female adapter. If the water delivery pipe is ¾ inch, use a ¾-inch female adapter.

5. Solder or solvent-weld (whichever is applicable) the air chamber to the reducer. If the water pipe is ½ inch, the air chamber should be at least 12 inches long. If the water pipe is ¾ inch, the air chamber should be at least 18 inches long.

6. Tighten the air chamber using two wrenches.

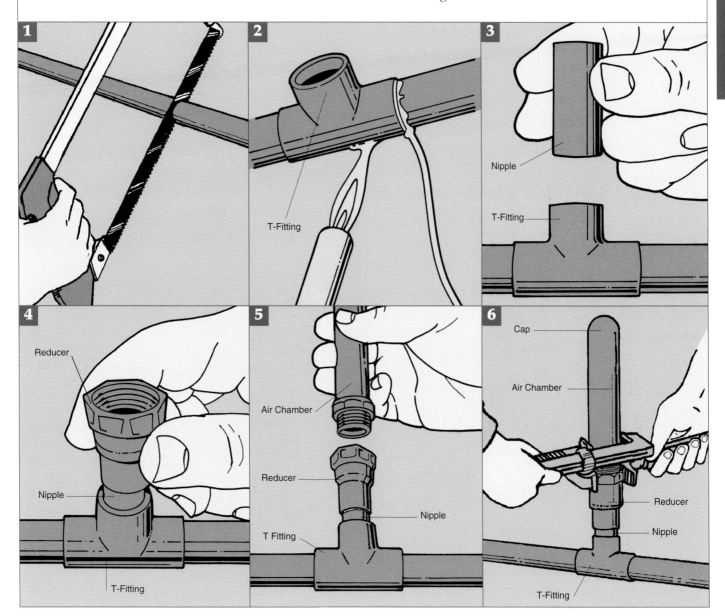

Repairing Copper Pipe

Before beginning, certain terms need to be clarified. One is the term "permanently repairing." There are various methods you can use to stop copper pipe or tubing from leaking, such as a special clamp that fits over the split. But all methods are temporary measures (see box below), except for cutting out the damaged piece and replacing it as described in this section.

The other terms that need clarification are "copper pipe" and "copper tubing." Although they are frequently used interchangeably, in this section the term "copper pipe" will apply to the rigid (hard-tempered) material that comes in straight lengths of 10 and 20 feet. The term "copper tubing" will apply to the flexible (soft-tempered) material that comes in coils of 10 to 60 feet.

Copper pipe and tubing are available in three grades: K, L, and M. The K is the heaviest; M is the thinnest; and L falls between the two. The M-grade copper pipe is used for water delivery in most homes. However, there are municipal plumbing codes that require the use of L- or K-grade copper pipe or copper tubing.

Each grade comes in various diameters, but the sizes usually required in home water delivery systems are ⅜, ½, ¾ or 1 inch. The size of a copper pipe or tubing is given as a nominal measurement. If you are going to use copper pipe and fittings that are going to be soldered, order material using the inner diameter. If you are going to use tubing and compression fittings, then order material using the outer diameter.

The easiest way to determine the grade, diameter, and hardness of the copper pipe or tubing you have in your house, and thus the kind you should buy to replace a piece that is leaking, is to cut off the damaged piece and take it to the plumbing supply, hardware, or home-center store. Store personnel can help you select the copper fitting you will need.

The fitting is the coupling, joint, or T-fitting, which is used to connect pipe or tubing together. A coupling has two ends. A T-fitting has three ends like the letter T. A joint (or elbow) is a curved connector that is used to attach two pieces of pipe or tubing where an angle of 45 or 90 degrees is necessary.

Temporary Repairs

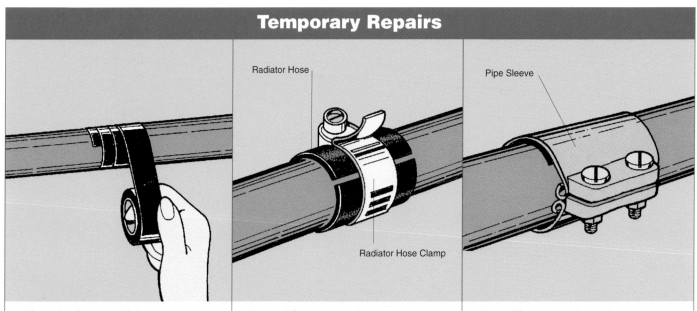

Radiator Hose

Radiator Hose Clamp

Pipe Sleeve

Electrical Tape. If there is a pinhole in a pipe, you can stop the leak temporarily by draining the pipe, drying it thoroughly, and wrapping layers of electrical tape around it. This repair is difficult to make work and is extremely temporary at best.

Hose Clamp. Another way to stop a copper pipe from leaking temporarily is with an auto radiator hose clamp and a piece of radiator hose that you have sliced open. Place the hose around the pipe so the opened end is opposite the leak, open the clamp and put it around the hose. Then tighten the clamp.

Pipe Sleeve. Still another temporary measure is the use of a pipe sleeve that is specifically made to stop a leak. This part can be obtained from a plumbing supply dealer or your local home center.

Preparing Pipe for Soldering

Close the main shutoff valve near the water meter or turn off the submersible pump. Flush toilets and open all faucets, including those on the outside of the house. Keep faucets open until the repair is completed and the water is turned on again.

1 Removing Old Pipe. Measure out at least 6 inches beyond each side of the split in the pipe or tubing. Lock the cutter onto the pipe or tubing at one measured spot and turn the tool one complete revolution. Tighten the cutter's handle and turn the tool again. Continue this way until the cut is completed.

Repeat the procedure where you measured on the other side of the damage. Work deliberately to make sure the ends of the pipe are cut squarely.

2 Cutting New Pipe. You now have to cut a length of replacement pipe or tubing that is the same size as the piece you removed. It is important to make sure that the end is square, so use the tubing cutter or hacksaw and miter box.

3 Removing Burrs. After cutting out the damaged pipe or tubing and the replacement, use a reamer to remove burrs from the ends of each piece of pipe or tubing—four ends in all.

4 Cleaning Pipes. The final step in preparation for soldering is to use emery cloth to polish the ends of all pieces and also the insides of the connectors. This will remove oxidation, which can affect the integrity of the soldered joints. Apply a thin coating of noncorrosive flux to the cleaned outside ends and to the insides of the fittings.

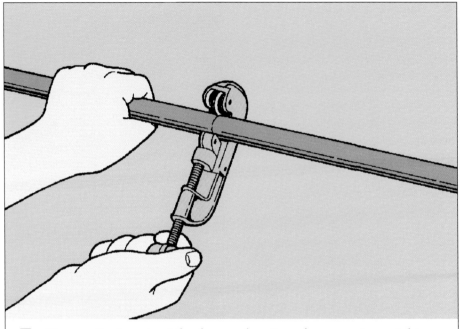

1 Use a cutter to cut out the damaged section of copper pipe or tubing. Remove at least 6 in., allowing at least 1 in. between the ends of the rupture and where you make the cut.

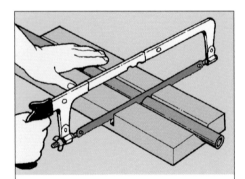

2 If a tube cutter is not available, use a miter box and hacksaw to insure that the ends will be square.

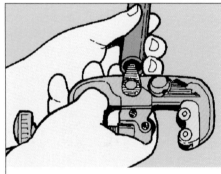

3 Remove burrs from the inside of copper pipe or tubing with a reamer, which may be a part of the cutter you've purchased.

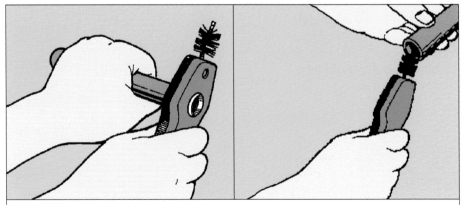

4 Clean the ends of all parts that will go together. This multipurpose tool features an abrasive for doing this, as well as a wire brush (left). The insides of the fitting and all pipes must be clean (right).

5 Removing Moisture from Pipe.
Pull down the ends of the pipe or tubing between which the replacement pipe will be connected to allow trapped water to drip out. If any droplets of water remain trapped, they will turn to steam as you apply heat and cause pinholes in the solder joint through which water will leak.

Roll some fresh white bread into a loose ball and push it into the pipe or tubing. Do not pack it tightly. Bread will absorb trapped droplets of water and prevent them from affecting the solder. When water is turned back on, the rush of water through the pipe or tubing will flush out the bread. Remove aerators from faucets so they do not block the passage of the bread.

6 Applying Flux. If the solder you are using does not contain flux, now is the time to apply it. Using a small brush, apply a light coating of flux to the ends of the existing pipe or tubing, to the ends of the replacement piece, and to the insides of the fittings.

7 Attaching Fittings. Slide the fittings onto the existing pipe or tubing, position the replacement piece in the opening, and move the fittings into place to couple the existing pipe or tubing to the replacement piece.

8 Soldering the Joint. Using the propane torch, heat the area around one of the joints as you hold the tip of the solder in the joint.

Caution: Wear heavy work gloves in case your hand comes into contact with the pipe or tubing, which may get extremely hot.

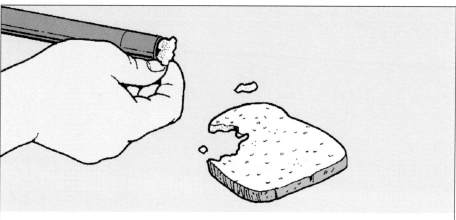

5 If a trickle of water persists, stuff white bread into the pipe or tubing to absorb trapped water.

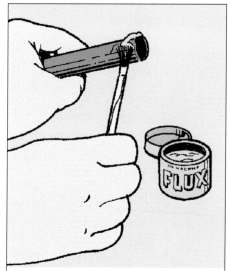

6 Apply a light coating of flux to the ends of the pipe or tubing. Flux inhibits oxidation as the pipe or tubing is being heated. Oxidation can prevent solder from taking hold, which will result in a leak.

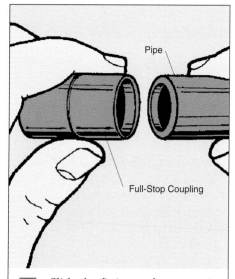

Pipe

Full-Stop Coupling

7 Slide the fitting as far as possible onto one end of the cut pipe. Then slip the other end of the cut pipe on the fitting, bottoming it out on the coupling stops.

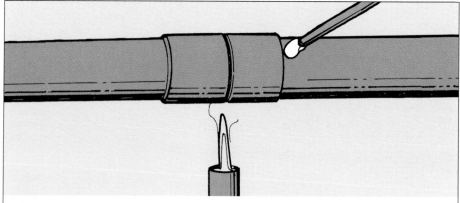

8 Heat the pipe for about five seconds. Then move the torch to the fitting as you hold the solder at the joint. The solder will melt and run into the joint to seal it.

9 Protecting Walls from Fire.

If you are soldering near a joist, wallboard, or some other material that is flammable, tack a cookie sheet over its surface. Always keep a fire extinguisher close by—just in case.

10 Removing Moisture from Pipe.

Do not apply the flame to the solder. As the pipe or tubing gets hot, the solder will run freely all the way around and into the joint. After the solder hardens, wipe the joint with a cold wet cloth to cool the pipe or tubing. Solder each joint this same way.

Solder & Flux

The National Standard Plumbing Code requires that solder and flux contain not more than 0.2 percent lead. Solder containing 50-percent lead and 50-percent tin (so-called solid-core 50:50 solder) was the standard for many years. The concern over the effect of lead on health, however, has resulted in an alteration of the formula. Your municipality may, in fact, have outlawed solder containing any lead. The alternative may be silver phosphorous solder.

The soldering method described here is the traditional one of fluxing and soldering as separate steps. (Soldering is also referred to as sweating.) Fluxing is necessary to prevent the formation of oxidation as heat is applied to the pipe.

Caution: Flux is an irritant. Wear eye protection and avoid rubbing your eyes. Wash hands thoroughly after working with flux and solder.

Some solder products already contain flux so you may not have to apply flux to the ends of the pipe or tubing as a separate step. Therefore, when you buy solder, read the instructions carefully or ask store personnel for help.

9 Do not take the chance of starting a fire. If you are soldering close to joists, wallboard, or other flammable material, tack a cookie sheet in place to serve as a barrier between the material and flame.

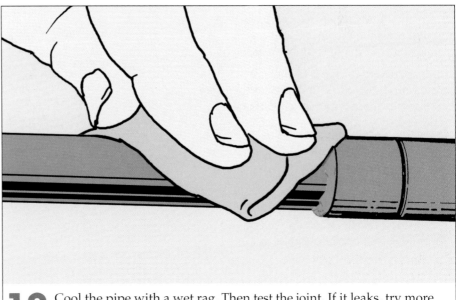

10 Cool the pipe with a wet rag. Then test the joint. If it leaks, try more solder, but in the end you may have to break the joint and try again.

Repairing CPVC Pipe

CPVC (chlorinated polyvinyl chloride) pipe is rigid. A replacement piece is joined to an existing pipe that has sprung a leak by cutting out the damaged section and installing the new piece of pipe using a process called solvent welding. Solvent cement is spread onto the ends of the pieces, which are joined together with CPVC fittings.

CPVC pipe is available in ½- and ¾-inch diameters and in 10-foot, and longer, lengths. It is rated to perform at temperatures up to 180°F under 100 pounds per square inch of pressure. Thus, CPVC meets the requirements necessary for pipe to carry hot water to plumbing fixtures and plumbing appliances.

CPVC pipe is not the only kind of plastic pipe used for water delivery. Where codes allowed, polybutylene (PB) was used, but this material is no longer manufactured. There is plenty of it still in place in homes. You can make repairs using copper or CPVC and transition fittings.

Another plastic pipe is cross-linked polyethylene (PEX). PEX meets code in many areas of the country and is routinely installed by professional plumbers. Make repairs using special fittings. In some area, crimp-ring fittings can be used in exposed locations; barbed fittings are necessary for in-wall installations.

Getting Ready

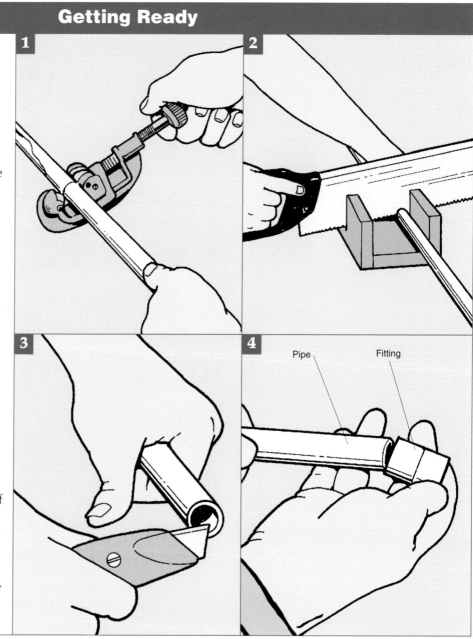

1. Flush toilets and open all faucets, including those on the outside of the house. Keep faucets open until the repair is completed and the water is turned on again.

Measure out at least 2 inches beyond each side of the leak. Lock a tubing cutter onto the pipe at one measured spot and turn the tool one complete revolution. Tighten the cutter's handle and turn again. Continue this way until the cut is completed.

Repeat the procedure where you measured on the other side of the damage. Make sure the ends of the pipe are cut squarely.

2. When the damaged section has been removed, measure the space between the two ends of the pipe. Cut a replacement piece of CPVC pipe to this size using a tubing cutter or backsaw and a miter box so the ends will be cut straight and smooth.

3. After cutting the replacement, use a utility knife to shave burrs off the ends of all pieces. Then bevel the edges to provide a secure weld.

4. Before applying primer and solvent cement, slip fittings on the ends of each pipe to make sure they slide freely.

Cementing CPVC

Caution: *Work in a ventilated area. Wear eye protection and gloves.*

1. The purpose of CPVC primer is to deglaze the parts that are going to be joined. Therefore, spread primer inside the fittings as well as around the ends of the pipes to the depth of the fitted socket.

2. While the primer is still wet, apply a coat of CPVC solvent cement to the ends of each pipe and to the insides of the fittings. Make sure the surfaces are completely covered.

3. Slide the fittings onto the replacement piece of pipe. Hold the replacement piece between the existing pipe, and bring fittings into place to make the replacement piece part of the water pipe.

Twist each fitting ¼ turn, then hold the parts tightly together for about 20 seconds before releasing. This action will evenly spread the solvent around the entire joint to ensure a tight fit.

4. Work quickly, but carefully, to get pieces locked together before the solvent hardens. The solvent cement will form a continuous bead all around the joints if the job is done properly.

5. If a continuous seal of solvent does not form, do the job again. The formation of an incomplete solvent seal will allow water to leak.

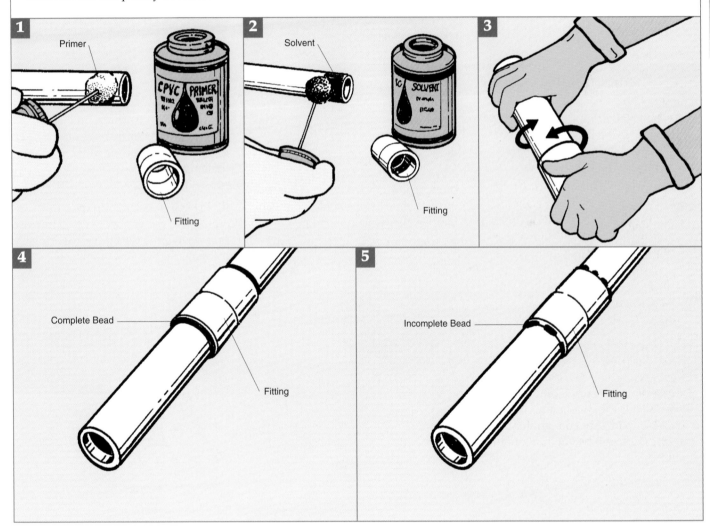

Repairing Galvanized-Steel Pipe

Galvanized-steel (also called "iron" or just "galvanized") water pipes can start to leak at the threads (black arrow) or in the body of the pipe (blue arrows).

Before making repairs, flush toilets and open all faucets, including those on the outside of the house. Keep faucets open until the repair is completed and the water is turned on again.

When water has stopped dripping from the threaded fitting, clean the circumference of the fitting using a piece of sandpaper. Work on the area until all corrosion has been eliminated and the fitting virtually gleams.

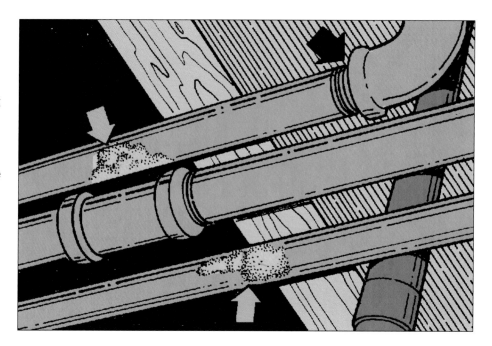

Temporary Repairs

A small leak around a threaded fitting or in the pipe's surface of a galvanized-steel water-delivery system may be stopped with a repair kit of epoxy.

1. Mix together the two-part epoxy contained in the repair kit. Read the package directions. Usually a repair patch is made by kneading together equal quantities of the two materials in the kit.

2. Form the compound into a rope and wrap it around the fitting, pressing it firmly into place. Give the material time to take hold—about an hour should do it.

3. If the leak is in the body of the pipe, the two-part repair patch described above, plus a pipe clamp, may stop it. After turning off the water, draining pipes, and cleaning the damaged area with sandpaper, press the epoxy patch over the leak.

4. Place the pipe clamp over the damage so the gasket of the clamp presses against the epoxy covering the leak. Tighten the clamp.

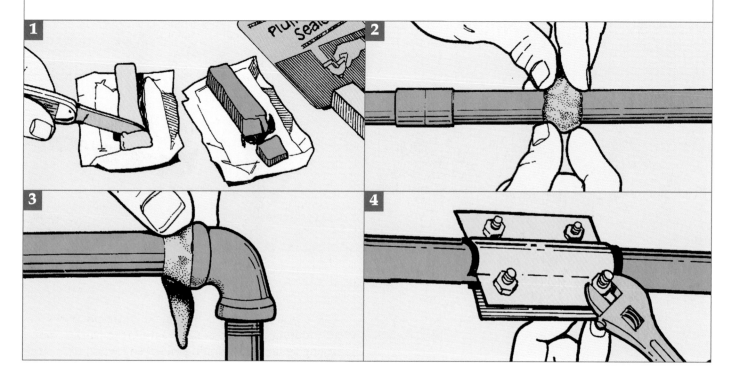

Permanent Repairs

After turning off the water and draining the pipes, follow these steps:

1 Measuring the Pipe. Measure and record the length of the pipe from the flange of one fitting to the flange of the other. Assuming the pipe diameter is ½ or ¾ inch, as is probably the case, add 1 inch to the measurement to allow for the ½ inch that the pipe extends into each fitting. If the pipe is 1 inch in diameter or larger, add 1¼ inches to the measurement to allow for an extension into each fitting of ⅝ inch. Take this measurement with you when you go to buy a replacement. The replacement parts you get—and a three-part union fitting—must equal the measurement.

2 Cutting Damaged Pipe. Use a reciprocating saw or hacksaw to cut the damaged pipe about 12 inches from one of the fittings.

3 Removing the Pipe. Grasp the fitting with one pipe wrench; grasp the short length of pipe with another pipe wrench. Position the wrenches so their jaws face each other. Hold the fitting tightly with one wrench and unscrew the pipe by turning the other wrench counter-clockwise. If the fitting is shot, unscrew that, too, and buy a new one.

4 Applying Penetrating Oil. If the threads of the pipe and fitting are so badly corroded that they will not move, apply penetrating oil. Give oil time to work and loosen things up before you try to separate the pipe and fitting. If oil does not work, heat the threaded area with a propane torch for about 30 seconds.

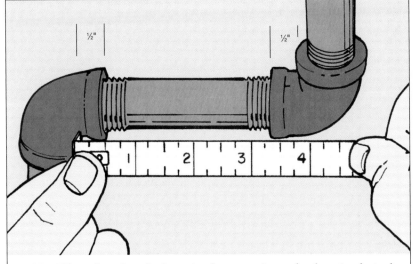

1 When figuring the length of a new piece of galvanized-steel pipe, be sure to allow 1 in. extra for the ½ in. that the pipe must extend into each fitting.

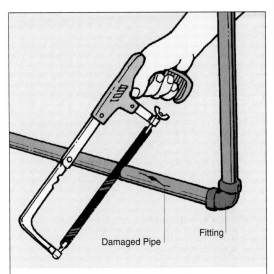

Damaged Pipe

Fitting

2 Cut the damaged section of pipe about 12 in. from one of the fittings with a hacksaw.

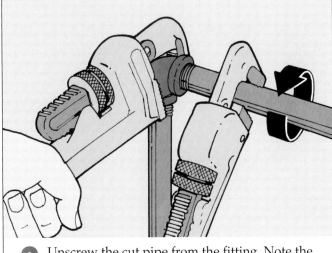

3 Unscrew the cut pipe from the fitting. Note the position of the wrenches.

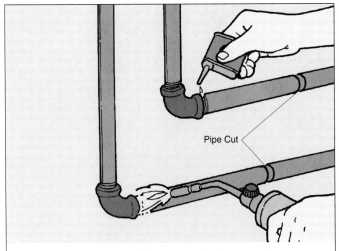

Pipe Cut

4 If you can't get the pipe to budge, apply penetrating oil to threads. Give it time to work before trying again. If penetrating oil doesn't work, try heat.

It should do the trick. But watch out for flammable material in the surrounding area. Tape a cookie sheet over the material to avoid trouble.

Cut the rest of the pipe off, but leave about 12 inches attached to the other fitting. Then remove that piece from the fitting in the same way.

5 **Replacing Pipe.** Replacing the section of pipe now becomes a matter of screwing together galvanized-steel nipples and three-part union connectors to equal the

length of the old pipe. It is impossible to insert a full length of pipe from one fitting to the other. In order to do this, you would have to disassemble the entire network from its terminus back to where you are working.

6 **Applying Joint Compound.** Let's start by assuming that you have to replace one or both of the fittings. Apply pipe joint compound to the threads of the adjacent pipes to which those fittings are screwed.

7 **Installing the Fitting.** Install the new fittings. Tighten them with the pipe wrenches, leaving them off-center about ⅛ inch to make it easier to get the other components into position.

Note: Be sure to apply pipe joint compound to male threads.

8 **Installing the Nipple.** Screw a galvanized-steel nipple to one of the fittings. Tighten the nipple. A nipple is a length of pipe 12 inches or less in length that is threaded externally on both ends.

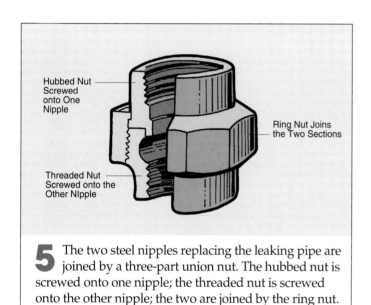

Hubbed Nut Screwed onto One Nipple

Ring Nut Joins the Two Sections

Threaded Nut Screwed onto the Other NIpple

5 The two steel nipples replacing the leaking pipe are joined by a three-part union nut. The hubbed nut is screwed onto one nipple; the threaded nut is screwed onto the other nipple; the two are joined by the ring nut.

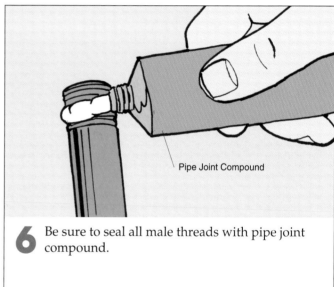

Pipe Joint Compound

6 Be sure to seal all male threads with pipe joint compound.

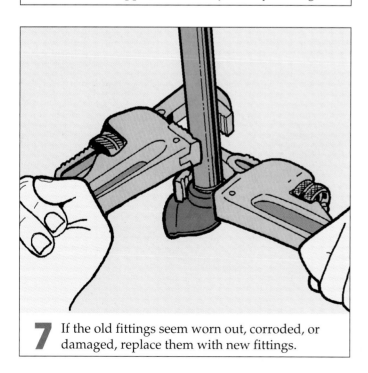

7 If the old fittings seem worn out, corroded, or damaged, replace them with new fittings.

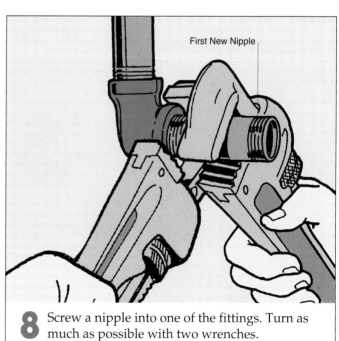

First New Nipple

8 Screw a nipple into one of the fittings. Turn as much as possible with two wrenches.

9 Positioning the Ring Nut.
Separate the three parts of a union connector, and place the large ring nut onto the nipple.

10 Attaching the Union Nut.
Screw the hubbed part of the three-part union nut onto the nipple. Apply pipe joint compound to the face of the hub. Working at the other fitting, screw a nipple into that.

11 Tightening the Union Nut.
Assuming that you are going to be using just two nipples and one three-part union nut, screw the third part of the union nut to this nipple. **Note:** This part of the union nut is externally threaded so the ring nut can be screwed to it.

12 Tightening the Ring Nut.
Turn both fittings so everything lines up and the lip of the hubbed part of the union nut fits into the externally threaded part of the union nut. Slide the ring nut into place, and tighten it securely to lock together the union nut and the nipples.

Following this procedure, you can screw together as many galvanized-steel nipples and three-part union nuts as it takes to cover the space left vacant between fittings.

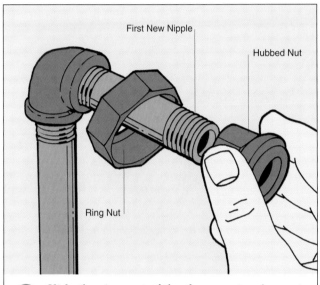

9 Slide the ring nut of the three-part union nut onto the nipple. Then screw the hubbed nut to the nipple and tighten it with two wrenches.

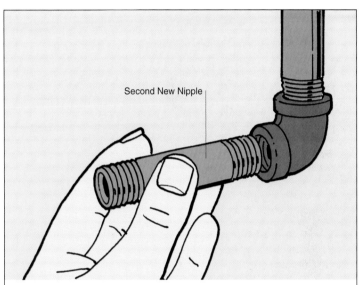

10 Screw another nipple into the fitting opposite the one you have assembled, and tighten it using one pipe wrench on the fitting and one on the new nipple.

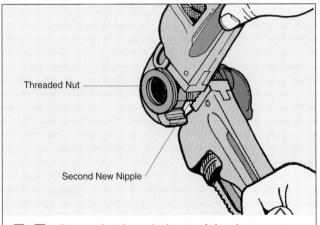

11 Screw the threaded nut of the three-part union nut onto this second nipple, which you just installed, and tighten the nut using two pipe wrenches.

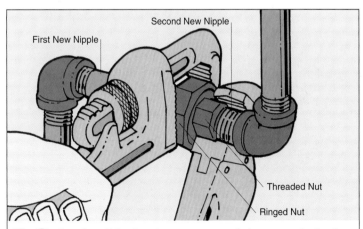

12 Lastly, slide the ring nut toward the second nipple, screw to threaded nut and tighten using two pipe wrenches—one to hold the threaded nut and one to turn the ring nut securely.

Repairing a Leaking Sink Trap

Sink traps come in various designs, such as the swivel P- or J-bend; may be metal or plastic; and may or may not have a cleanout plug. Another version is a fixed P-trap that is connected directly to the drainpipe rather than to an elbow.

Temporary Repair

If the metal trap of a sink corrodes and begins to leak, try a temporary repair using plastic, waterproof, stretchable tape—the type used for repairing garden hoses. Wrap several layers of tape around the trap. It should stop the leak for a few days. Keep a bucket under the trap—just in case.

Permanent Repair

You can replace a corroded metal trap with another or one made of plastic. An advantage of plastic is that it will resist corrosion. Here's how to proceed.

Place a pail under the trap. By hand, try to unscrew the locknuts holding the trap to the tailpiece and extension. If you cannot budge them, use adjustable pliers or a pipe wrench to free them. Then, unscrew the slipnuts and remove the old corroded trap.

Stuff a rag into the drainpipe extension to prevent sewer gas from entering the room. Take the trap with you to ensure that you buy a replacement of the same shape and dimensions. Lavatory traps are normally 1¼ inches in diameter, while sink traps are 1½ inches in diameter.

Install the new trap after lubricating the threaded surfaces. You need to tighten pastic slipnuts by hand only. Then run the water. If there is seepage, tighten slipnuts just a bit with adjustable pliers or a pipe wrench. Use a wrench to tighten chrome slipnuts.

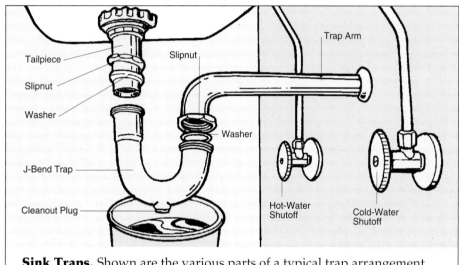

Sink Traps. Shown are the various parts of a typical trap arrangement. The trap may or may not have a cleanout plug.

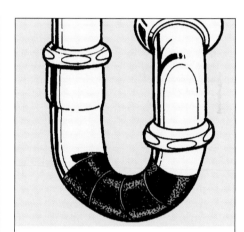

Temporary Repairs. Wrapping a few layers of waterproof plastic tape around a corroded trap may stop the leak temporarily.

Permanent Repairs. This sequence shows the steps to take when replacing a trap (from left): loosen slipnuts; remove and discard the old trap; install the new trap, tighten the slipnuts.

improvements

Removing an Old Lavatory from the Vanity

The information in this section pertains to those who are making a one-for-one lavatory exchange. This means that the old lavatory (either as part of the vanity, or a wall-hung unit) is being replaced with a similar-size lavatory.Those who are installing a lavatory that is larger than the one being replaced must enlarge the hole in the vanity countertop to accommodate the larger lav.

Turn off the water. Using an adjustable wrench or basin wrench, loosen the nuts holding hot- and cold-water risers to the faucet. Place a pail under the risers to collect the water. Place a pail under the trap, and use a spud wrench or adjustable pliers to loosen trap coupling nuts. Remove the trap, and stuff a rag in the drain stub-out to block sewer gases.

Release the stopper. If you are removing a rimmed lavatory, look for basin clips under the vanity top (Figure 1). These clips secure the lavatory to the vanity by locking into tabs. The tabs are slotted so they can be easily loosened or tightened with a screwdriver. Remove the basin clips by turning the bolts counterclockwise.

Apply pressure from below to loosen the lavatory from the vanity. If the lavatory is stuck in place, use a utility knife to score the plumber's putty or silicone seal between the lavatory and vanity. Cast-iron units installed with rims are heavy. Support the unit carefully, and do not drop it.

If the existing hardware (faucet, drain, tailpiece, and stopper) is to be reused, remove them from the old lavatory.

Installing a New Lavatory in a Vanity

Install the faucet. When installing a rimmed lavatory, turn it upside down and use a screwdriver to push rim tabs (if they are used) inward until each is at a 90-degree angle to the rim (Figure 2). This is a good time to hook up the faucet assembly as well. Do not put too much pressure on the wrench when you assemble the faucet, as it could crack the lavatory.

A ⅛-inch-wide bead of silicone caulking should be applied around

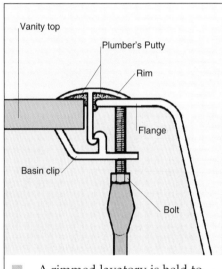

1 A rimmed lavatory is held to the vanity with clips. To release the clips, loosen the bolts.

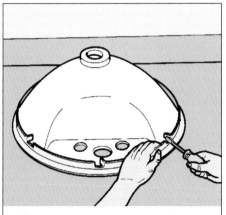

2 The tabs that may be found on a new rimmed lavatory should be pushed in until they form a 90-degree angle.

the edge of the vanity's opening before dropping in the lavatory. (Do this for both rimmed and non-rimmed lavatories.)

Press the lavatory down into the silicone caulking. With a rimmed lavatory, it will be necessary to maintain the pressure while installing all the basin clips. To accomplish this, tie a length of rope around a 2x4. Then, place the 2x4 across the lavatory, and fish the rope through the drain hole. Tie a brick around the end of the rope (Figure 3). The basin clips can be installed. Be sure they lock with the rim tabs. Remove the brick, rope, and 2x4.

Connect the hot- and cold-water risers; drain the tailpiece, trap, and stopper. Run the water, and check for leaks.

Replacing a Wall-Hung Lavatory

Inspect the wall-hung lavatory that is to be replaced. Determine how it has been mounted by checking the under-side of the unit at both rear corners. If the lavatory was installed with bolts, put something under the unit to support it. Release the fixture by removing the bolts (Figure 1 opposite).

You may find slots cut into each corner of the rear edge of the lavatory

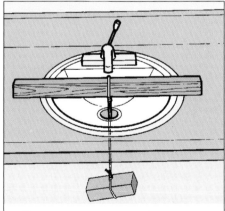

3 Use this setup to keep a newly installed rimmed lavatory secure while you install basin clips.

(Figure 2). The slots intersect with tabs that are connected to a bracket and screwed into the wall. This type of unit must be lifted off the bracket.

The lavatory may have been installed with self-contained lugs (Figure 3). In this case, it must be lifted off the bracket.

If the new lavatory uses the same type of retention method as the old lavatory, mount it the same way. However, if retainers are different, remove the existing one and install the new one (Figure 4). Use these guidelines when mounting a wall-hung lavatory:

Notice the holes left in the wall by the existing retainer. They are probably spaced 16 inches apart. If the screws that held the retainer to the wall were screwed into the studs, the new retainer can be attached the same way. However, if the screws do not reach the studs, you will have to use toggle bolts. Be sure they are long and strong enough to support the weight of the new lavatory.

Lavatories are normally positioned 31 to 34 inches floor to rim. Be sure to allow for the distance between the slots or lugs of the lavatory and the top of the lavatory rim when deciding

upon the height at which the lavatory will be hung. Otherwise, the lavatory will be hung too high.

Hold the retainer up to the wall at the correct height, and secure one end of it to the wall. Place a carpenter's level across the retainer. An assistant will have to hold the level steady to keep it from slipping as you maneuver the retainer up or down until the carpenter's level shows that it is straight. At this point, screw the other end of the retainer to the wall, and mount the lavatory.

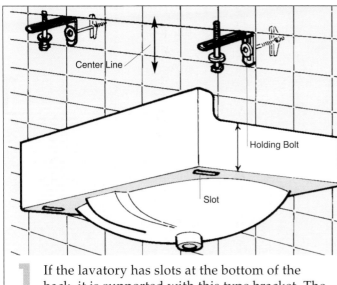

1 If the lavatory has slots at the bottom of the back, it is supported with this type bracket. The holding bolts are adjusted for level.

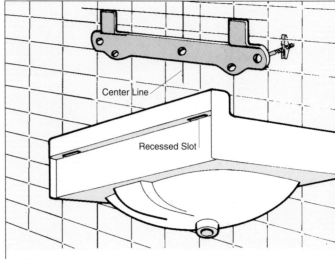

2 In this lavatory, recessed slots are also used for bracket assembly. The bowl is simply placed over the bracket assembly.

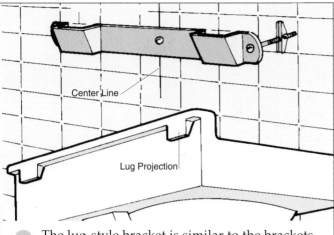

3 The lug-style bracket is similar to the brackets shown above. In this setup, the bowl lugs slip into the bracket assembly.

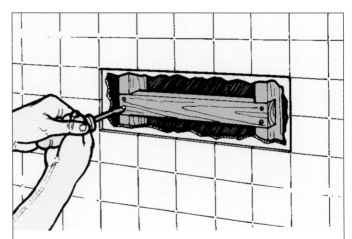

4 To secure a bracket that cannot be attached to the studs with screws, a horizontal framing piece can be mortised into the studs.

Replacing a Bathtub

Replacing a bathtub is not easy. Most likely, the job will require cutting into a wall to reach the pipes. You may even have to remove a wall in order to take out the old tub and fit the new tub into the room.

Removing the Old Tub

Turn off the water. Remove the faucets, spout, and diverter. In order to expose the pipes, a wall (in the adjacent room or closet behind the bathtub) may have to be removed (Figure 1). If this cannot be done, remove the ceramic tile or the plastic panel, and cut away the plaster or drywall (gypsum wallboard) subwall.

Disconnect the waste pipe, overflow, and water pipes serving the tub.

Chip out one course of ceramic tile around the perimeter of the tub, or remove the plastic panels covering the walls (Figure 3).

Move the tub away from the wall. This may be difficult. If the tub will not budge, it may be held to the wall framing with retaining clips. Remove as much of the wall as is necessary (Figure 4) to reach and remove the clips (Figures 5 and 6).

The tub may fit through the door-way—try standing it on end. To move the tub across the floor, place a few 2x4s or leftover carpeting or flooring (of suitable size) under it for use as skid strips (Figure 7) to protect the floor while making it easier to move the tub.

The alternative to getting the tub through the doorway is to cut down a wall (Figure 8). This involves cutting away studs to form a hole in the wall. Avoid cutting into a wall that is loadbearing. Nail 2x4s and 2x6s to the studs to help shore up the framing.

Installing the New Tub

When the new tub is moved into place, make sure it is level, using shims if necessary. Attach retaining clips, if necessary. (The tub may or may not require clips depending upon the manufacturer.) Use silicone caulking (Figures 9 and 10) to produce a caulk bead that will fill the joint. Let it dry overnight. Then connect the plumbing; check for leaks; and perform the necessary carpentry and wall-finishing work to get the room back into shape.

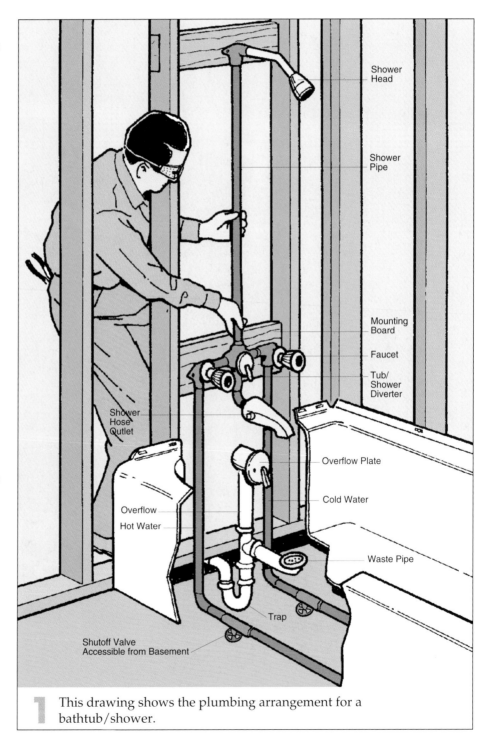

Shower Head

Shower Pipe

Mounting Board

Faucet

Tub/ Shower Diverter

Shower Hose Outlet

Overflow Plate

Cold Water

Overflow

Hot Water

Waste Pipe

Trap

Shutoff Valve Accessible from Basement

1 This drawing shows the plumbing arrangement for a bathtub/shower.

2 Disconnect the drain, waste pipe, and overflow pipe by loosening locknuts with adjustable pliers or a wrench.

3 If the walls are tiled, chip out a course of ceramic tile around the perimeter of the tub.

4 It may be necessary to remove more tile than shown in Figure 3. It may also be necessary to remove floor tiles.

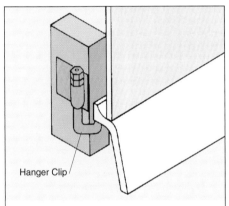

5 If the tub is held with hanger clips, they must be loosened or removed before the tub can be taken out.

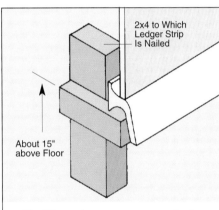

6 The tub may rest on a ledger strip, as shown here. If so, simply take off the strip when removing the old tub.

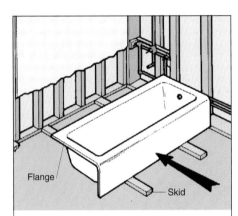

7 Use skid strips or a piece of carpeting or sheet flooring to move the tub and protect the floor.

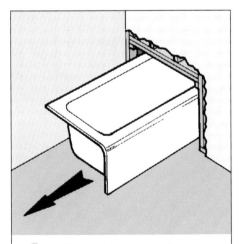

8 If the bathtub won't fit through the doorway, make a hole just large enough for the tub to pass through.

9 With the tub in place, install cement backer board. Then tile, grout, and apply a bead of tub and tile caulk.

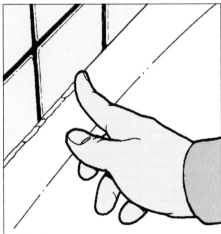

10 Smooth the caulk with a wet finger. Then use a damp cloth to wipe off any excess.

Installing a Dishwasher

The installation of a dishwasher requires carpentry skills, electrical skills, and plumbing skills. The best place to install a dishwasher is in a cabinet by the kitchen sink (Figure 1).

Check the appliance manufacturer's instructions concerning the plumbing rough-in and electrical requirements. The following guidelines will help you accomplish this project.

Note: The recommendations offered here are meant to augment the manufacturer's instructions—not to supersede them.

Guidelines

Consult your local plumbing codes before beginning work. Some regulations are practically standard. Two such regulations are: The use of minimum ⅜-inch copper pipe for the water-supply line and the use of ½-inch copper pipe or PVC pipe for the drain.

Restrictions concerning vents, traps, and types of piping vary from municipality to municipality.

Similarly, electric work should be done in accordance with the National Electrical Code and the modifications to that code enacted by authorities in your area (Figure 2).

Installation

Although it may not be suggested by the dishwasher manufacturer, it is wise to have the dishwasher on its own circuit.

An average-size dishwasher needs a 24-inch-wide by 21-inch-deep space. Modify a cabinet near the kitchen sink.

Turn the water off. Cut the sink's hot water pipe below the shutoff valve which serves the sink's hot water faucet. Solder a copper T-fitting to the pipe.

Use ⅜-inch copper pipe or flexible supply to extend the water supply from the T-fitting to the dishwasher. Include a shutoff valve.

Note: A shutoff valve built into the water pipe of the dishwasher is required by code. When a repair must be made, turn off the water to the dishwasher without turning off water to the entire house.

The dishwasher can drain into the sink's drain. A T-fitting with a ½-inch branch is made especially for this purpose.

If a waste-disposal unit exists, have the dishwasher drain into the disposal (Figure 4). Usually this requires the removal of a plug covering an inlet located on the disposal unit. A fitting to secure the disposal to the ½-inch drainpipe can be obtained from an appliance or plumbing-supply store. Also, a kit containing all necessary drainage parts may be available for your appliance.

If the local plumbing codes require, extend the drainpipe from the kitchen drain or waste-disposal unit to an air gap and from the air gap to the dishwasher (Figure 5). The purpose of the air gap is to prevent water from siphoning in from the kitchen drain to the dishwasher. If an air gap is not used, loop the hose and connect it to the bottom of the countertop.

Connect the water-supply line, drain line, and electrical power supply to the dishwasher (Figure 6).

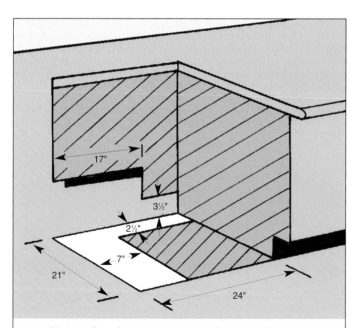

1 Using this drawing as a guide, modify a cabinet to accept the dishwasher. Areas not shaded are available for dishwasher water-supply piping and drain lines.

2 Bore a hole (large enough to accommodate the drain, water, and power lines) into the side panel of the sink cabinet. Shut off the electricity, and run a cable from a 20-amp grounded circuit.

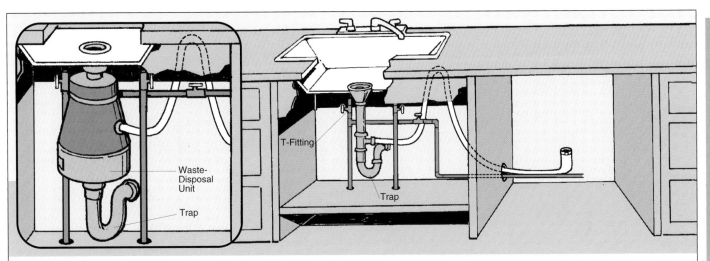

Dishwasher
Shutoff Valve

T-Fitting from Hot-Water Line   To Dishwasher

3 Install a water-supply line with a shutoff valve (two alternative hookups are shown), and then run copper tubing into the cabinet space.

Waste-
Disposal
Unit

T-Fitting

Trap

Trap

4 The dishwasher can drain either through a waste-disposal unit or directly into the sink drainage network. If an air-gap fitting is not used (Figure 5), loop or connect the hose to the countertop using a clamp.

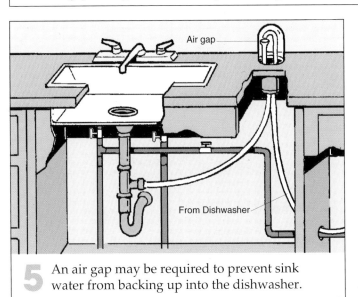

Air gap

From Dishwasher

5 An air gap may be required to prevent sink water from backing up into the dishwasher.

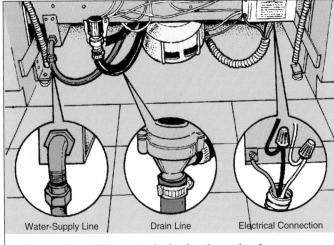

Water-Supply Line   Drain Line   Electrical Connection

6 Final installation includes hookups for the water-supply line, the drain line, and the electrical power.

Ion-Exchange Water Softeners

Rare is a community that enjoys soft water. Rarer still is a well-water system with soft water. Most water has some degree of hardness, measured in grains by a water-hardness test. Hard water contains high levels of calcium and magnesium ions, which are easily attracted to metal and other surfaces to form a crusty scale. Also, detergents and soaps don't perform efficiently in hard water because they react with the metal ions. If you notice a lack of sudsing when you wash or you notice the formation of scale in your tea kettle or on the tile or shower doors in your bathroom, your water is most likely hard.

The surest way to tell whether you have hard water is to have the water tested. A basic water analysis for a softening system should include tests for total hardness, iron level, pH, and total dissolved solids (TDS). Your local plumbing-supply dealer can perform the tests and likely has statistics on the local water. If you find that the water is hard, the fix is easy: install an ion-exchange water softener (Figure 1).

Ion-exchange softeners work by exchanging calcium and magnesium ions for sodium or potassium ions (from sodium chloride or potassium chloride used in conjunction with a regenerating resin). Softeners do not remove impurities from water or produce "pure" water, however. Armed with knowledge from the tests, the dealer can steer you to the correct unit for your water. Ion-exchange softeners cost $1,000 and up, installed. But you can save the labor costs by installing the system yourself.

Before you buy a softener, check your house's water pressure. The pressure should be between 30 and 100 pounds per square inch (psi). Low pressure causes inefficient softener performance and frequent regeneration; high pressure can cause damage to the system, voiding the softener's warranty. If you're on a municipal water-supply system, high pressure can be lowered with a pressure-reducing valve installed upstream of the softener. On a well-water system, a qualified technician can raise or lower the pressure by adjusting the pressure tank's setting.

Two kinds of water softeners are available, those that you regenerate at home (either manually or automatically) and those exchanged and regenerated by a soft-water service organization. For home regeneration, your water-supply system must supply ample water for

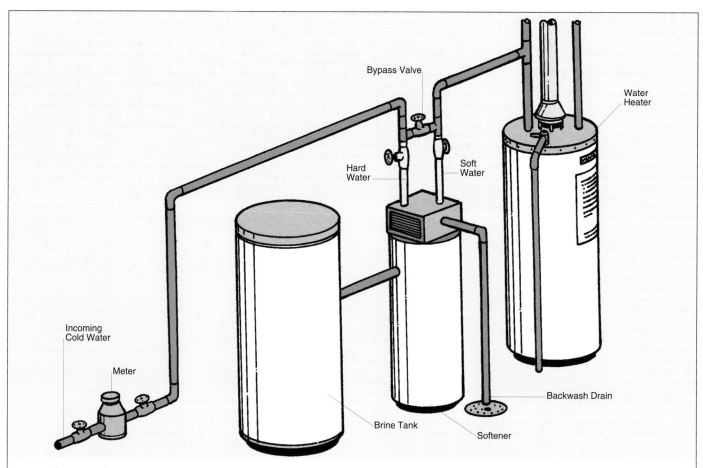

1 The complete water softener installation for home-regeneration includes the softener, its valving, a brine tank, and a drain for the briny backwash. Some home systems don't have a separate brine tank.

softener regeneration—at least 3 gallons a minute at 20 psi. An automatic softener needs (within reach) a 120-volt three-slot electrical outlet connected to a ground fault circuit interrupter (GFCI).

Where to drain the regeneration effluent is an important consideration in what type of softener you choose. Home-regenerated softeners need a place to drain their briny backwash. In most locales, you cannot run softener backwash into a public sewer. Some codes will, though, let it be run into a home septic system or a dry well or out on the ground as gray water. In no case should effluent be allowed to run onto a neighbor's property.

A softener for home regeneration also needs access for bringing in the 40- to 60-pound bags of softener salt, plus space above the brine tank to maneuver them. Moreover, the brine tank itself should have a flat surface to rest on. A commercially-serviced softener has fewer demands but does need access for periodic tank exchanges.

Other considerations include providing a protected location free from freezing. If the tank is not metal,

protection from sunlight is important. You will also want to have easy access to every part of the system for repair or replacement, when necessary.

Where to Distribute Soft Water

Where you connect the softener into the house's cold-water main determines which parts of the house get softened and which do not. Because the softener is usually installed upstream of the water heater, the hot water to every fixture will be softened. Some installations stop there. It is preferable—especially if the water is really hard—to provide both hot and cold softened water for bathing, laundry, and dish washing. Because some toilets use a lot of water, softening of toilet flush water is nice, but costly. For this reason, toilet water is often not softened. Likewise, outdoor water should not be softened. It is best not to drink much water softened with sodium ions (from sodium chloride). Heart patients are usually advised not to drink it at all. Ideally, a special tap would deliver untreated water just for drinking.

In the basement, utility room, or crawl space, trace your home's cold-water system from the water-main entrance to the water heater. Somewhere between these is where you'll most likely install the softener. Choose your softener location carefully to provide soft water where you want it and leave the untreated water elsewhere. For example, if the house sillcock and toilets all take off the cold-water main shortly after it enters the house, you could tap the main just beyond the last such branch and install the softener there. That way, no toilet or outdoor water lines would get soft water and every other home line would.

Installing the Piping

You will need to install new pipes that tap into the cold-water main and branch off to a softener inlet, a softener outlet, and a bypass. As you might expect, the inlet connects to the piping coming from the water meter, the outlet attaches to the piping going toward the water heater, and the bypass replaces the portion of the house main you removed (Figure 2). For water control, all the connections are fitted with gate valves. (Some local codes approve ball valves and

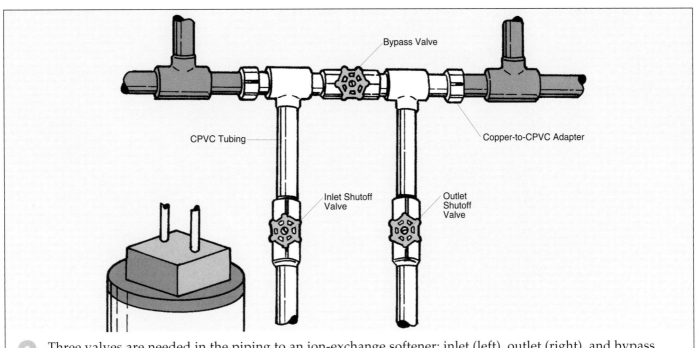

2 Three valves are needed in the piping to an ion-exchange softener: inlet (left), outlet (right), and bypass (center).

sometimes globe valves for the bypass.)

The piping and fittings you will need depend on what kind of pipes your house has—galvanized steel, copper, or plastic tubing—and what type of piping you use for the softener connection. Chlorinated polyvinyl chloride (CPVC) plastic tubing is by far the easiest material to work with. It may be joined either by solvent-welding or by using hand-tightened O-ring fittings. To connect solvent-welded CPVC to copper or galvanized piping, you will need the proper transition adapters. (Hand-tightened O-ring fittings serve as transition adapters to copper tubing.)

Use the same size piping as that of the house's cold-water main—usually ¾-inch. If the main is ½ inch, you will need to use transitions to match the typical ¾-inch pipe connections at the softener. Whatever piping system you use, provide two unions at the connection to the water softener. The unions will allow the softener to be removed and replaced without

disturbing the piping.

Unpack the softener and its accessories, making sure you received everything and that nothing is damaged. Following instructions, complete any final assembly of softener components. The control valve may need to be mounted; the resin poured in; a bypass valve fitted; and other accessories installed.

Beneath the spot where you will open the house's cold-water piping, place a pail to catch any remaining water in the system. Measure between the inlet and outlet on your softener; add two inches to this; and cut out a piece of copper or plastic cold-water main a few inches longer than the measurement (Figure 3). Use a tubing cutter or hacksaw.

CAUTION: If you replace a section of metal pipe with plastic pipe using CPVC-to-copper adapters and this portion of the house-water piping is used as an electrical service ground, you must bridge across the plastic portion of piping with a length of No. 6

copper wire (for a house with up to 200-ampere electrical service) connected with two UL-listed ground clamps.

On galvanized piping, saw through in one spot with a hacksaw, allowing you to unthread the sections of pipe on both sides of the cut back to the threaded fittings. Install threads-to-CPVC transition adapters in each of those fittings and tighten. You are now ready to run CPVC tubing to the softener.

Using solvent cement, assemble lengths of CPVC tubing, T-fittings, and valves to create a valved inlet, outlet, and bypass (Figure 4). Or, you can assemble CPVC tubes using O-ring fittings. Be sure the incoming water routes to the softener's inlet. If the valves have flow arrows, see that they are properly positioned.

For filling the softener tank, set the three valves as follows: inlet open, outlet and bypass closed. Position the softener beneath the new piping (Figure 5), and finish running CPVC

3 Cut through a copper or plastic cold-water main near the softener location, removing a section about 3 inches longer than the separation between the softener's inlet and outlet stubs.

Mini Tubing Cutter

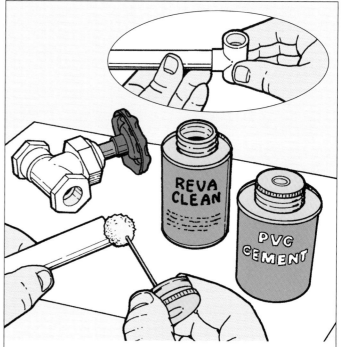

4 To join tubes to fittings by solvent-welding, use the cleaner solution on all parts, apply solvent cement to the tube end and fitting socket, and then join the tube and fitting immediately (inset).

REVA CLEAN

PVC CEMENT

5 Wrestle the softener into position, centered beneath the inlet and outlet pipes, and then connect the unit using male or female transition unions.

tubing to it. Be sure to follow any specific instructions with the softener you get.

Run the softener's backwash line between the drain fitting on the softener valve and a suitable drain. Provide a 1½-inch air gap between the drain line and the drain (Figure 6).

Position the brine tank and fill it with the proper softener salt. Plug the control cord (if there is one) into a suitable electrical outlet. Place the softener's control valve in the backwash position.

CAUTION: Disinfect the softener according to manufacturer's instructions before any of the softener's water gets into your house piping. Disinfection involves adding a measured amount of disinfectant, usually household bleach, to the softener tank and waiting the required time before flushing it out. Be sure all disinfectant has been removed before opening the softener's outlet valve.

Crack open the house shutoff valve slightly. Air should begin escaping slowly from the backwash line. If water rushes in too rapidly, some resin may be washed out, so if you notice any resin coming out, slow the flow of water. When all air has been purged from the softener tank, you can open the valve fully. Let water drain from the backwash line until it flows clear. Place the control valve in the softening position and check for leaks. Open the outlet valve to purge the house piping of air. Starting on the lowest story, close the faucets as water flows steadily from them. When all are closed, check again for leaks.

For softening, open the inlet and outlet valves, and close the bypass valve. For servicing, close the inlet and outlet valves, and open the bypass valve. While automatic softeners have built-in bypass valves, a manual bypass valve is needed if the softener is removed for servicing.

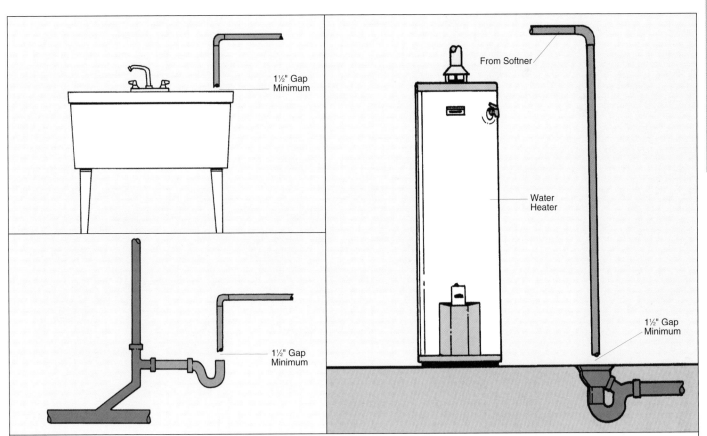

6 Provide a 1½-inch air gap at the softening system's backwash drain to prevent any cross connection between briny effluent and your potable water-supply system.

Relocating a Toilet

The following guidelines demonstrate how to move an existing toilet from one location to another. You can also use this information to install a new toilet where one does not exist, such as in a newly remodeled bathroom or in an addition.

Turn the water off. Before you begin, consider how the toilet will be vented. Consult plumbing codes for the allowable distances of the closet bend and soil pipe to the vent. For example, the same DWV setup can be used if you're placing the toilet less than 6 feet away from a vent.

Flush the toilet. Then use a large sponge to remove water left in the bowl and in the tank.

Remove the caps that cover the bowl hold-down bolts. Use a wrench to remove the nuts from the bolts.

Working at the water-supply line (riser), use pipe and/or adjustable wrenches to remove the riser and the water shutoff valve.

The tank and bowl of a two-piece toilet must be uncoupled. Wiggle the bowl until it breaks free from the floor. Stuff a rag into the closet bend. Place the toilet aside, handling it carefully. If it is dropped, the bowl and tank may crack (Figure 1).

Cut the water-supply line so its end is beneath the floor or inside the wall. Cap the end of the pipe. Then trace the line back to the place it intersects the water pipe, and remove it. The water-supply line for the relocated toilet should be spliced in at this point.

Undo the screws holding the closet bend flange to the floor, and remove the flange (Figure 2).

Determine whether the new location for the toilet will allow you to tie a closet bend into the existing soil pipe. Otherwise, the existing soil pipe has to be sealed and a new setup installed. If this is the case, use a hacksaw to cut off the existing closet bend and as much of the soil pipe as necessary. To install a new DWV setup, cap the old soil pipe; cut into the home's main drainpipe; and connect a fitting. Then, extend the new soil pipe from where the toilet is going to be to the main drain, and extend the soil pipe up through the house and through the roof for venting. The area where the pipe goes through the roof must be sealed with roof cement and flashing.

Cover the hole in the floor with underlayment in preparation for laying new floor covering. If the new floor covering is not going to be installed right away, place a piece of plywood over the hole to prevent an accident.

Setting Up the New Location

Indicate the location for the new toilet. Use a framing square to draw a baseline on the floor at a 90-degree angle to the wall in the place where the toilet is to go (Figure 3). Center the bowl over this baseline, and draw an outline of the base of the bowl onto the floor (Figure 4). Remove the bowl, and measure to make sure the baseline is equidistant between the end lines of the outline.

Lay the toilet on its side. Measure the distance from the rear or front of the bowl to the center of the horn (Figure 5). Transpose this measurement onto the baseline (Figure 6).

Measure the diameter of the pipe tailpiece of a new closet bend flange, and transpose that onto the

1 Handle the tank and bowl with care. Place them in a safe spot while preparing for installation. If dropped, the toilet may crack.

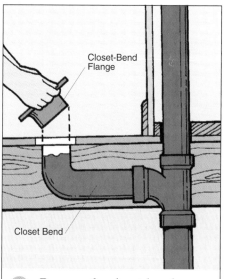

Closet-Bend Flange

Closet Bend

2 Remove the closet-bend flange. Cut the closet bend, and either seal the opening or attach and extend a new bend.

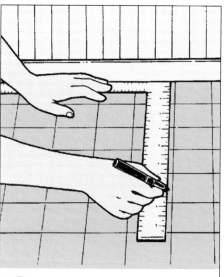

3 Draw a baseline for the new toilet. The reference line should be square to the wall and should indicate the center of the toilet.

floor. Check and double-check the measurements before cutting a hole in the floor.

Drill a pilot hole in the floor (Figure 7). Use this as a starting point for cutting the hole for the closet bend (Figure 8).

Install the new flooring (this may already have been done).

Insert the closet bend through the hole so the flange rests on the floor (Figure 9). Screw the flange to the floor. Connect the closet bend to the soil pipe (Figure 10, page 92). Install hold-down bolts, and place a wax seal around the bowl's horn (Figure 11, page 92). Then, mount the toilet.

Use a carpenter's square to make sure the bowl is level (Figure 12, page 92). If it is not level, place a small nonferrous metal shim under the segment of the bowl that makes the bubble of the level center itself, thereby indicating that the bowl is true. Tighten the nuts to the hold-down bolts. Seal the rim with silicone caulking.

Extend the water-supply line; seal connections; turn on the water; and check for leaks.

4 Draw an outline of the base of the bowl onto the floor.

5 Determine the position of the center of the horn.

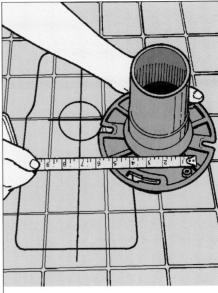

6 Establish the center of the horn on the floor. The closet bend will fit into this space.

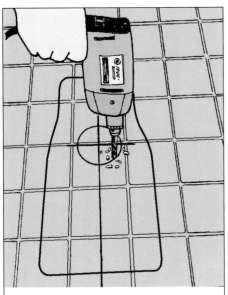

7 Drill a pilot hole. Then remove the tiles from the circle using a cold chisel.

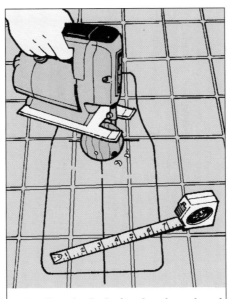

8 Cut the hole for the closet bend and flange using a saber saw.

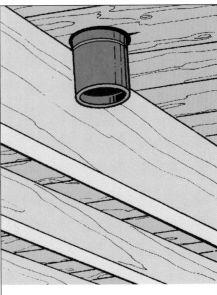

9 Insert the flange and its extension so that the extension drops into the basement.

Continued on page 92

Continued from page 91

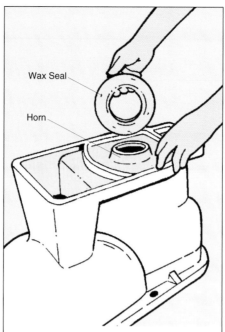

10 Attach the closet bend and extend the waste pipe to tie the toilet's flange extension into the most convenient soil pipe.

11 To seal the bowl, press the wax seal to the bowl's horn so it sticks. Then hold the bowl right-side up, and place it in position.

12 Make sure the bowl is level. Then tighten the nuts to the hold-down bolts. Seal around the rim with silicone caulking.

Installing a Bidet

Installing a bidet is similar to installing a toilet. Both cold- and hot-water pipes will be necessary. When positioning the bidet in the bathroom, allow 2 inches between the back of the bidet and the wall against which it is going (right). A closet bend is not necessary; instead use an ordinary lavatory or sink trap. Cut and insert a T-fitting in an existing soil pipe, and extend the bidet drainpipe to it.

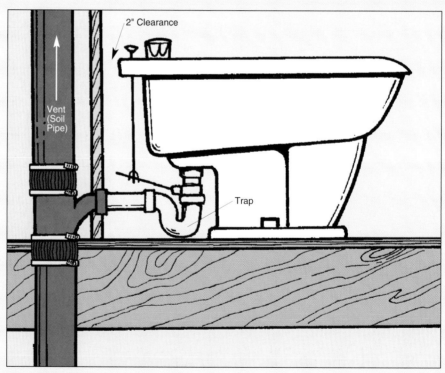

Bidet Installation. This diagram illustrates the typical DWV requirements for a bidet.

Installing an Electric Water Heater

With the exception of disconnecting electricity from a leaking water heater and connecting electricity to a new water heater, installing an electric water heater is done pretty much the same way as installing a gas water heater.

The only other exception is that there is no flue to contend with when you're replacing an electric water heater.

CAUTION: It is imperative for your safety that the first thing you do before tackling this job is to remove the water heater fuse or switch off the water heater circuit breaker in the fuse or main circuit breaker panel. Do not restore electrical service to the water heater until the new unit is in place, filled, and electrically grounded (see below).

If you aren't sure which fuse or circuit breaker belongs to the water heater and you don't know how to use a circuit tester to verify that electricity to the water heater has been turned off, do not attempt to replace the water heater. The presence of high voltage can kill you.

Hooking Up An Electric Water Heater

Proceed as follows:

After establishing that water on the floor is the result of a leak and not condensation, turn off the electricity and proceed.

Remove the cover from the spot on the old tank where the power cable from the fuse or circuit breaker panel enters the tank (Figure 1). Notice that wires of the power cable are color-coded. A bare copper or green wire is ground; a black or red wire is the hot wire; a white wire or a black-and-white wire is neutral.

The wires of the power cable are probably connected by wire connectors to the wires that are attached to the thermostats. Unscrew the wire connectors to disconnect the power cable wires from the thermostat wires. Test the black (hot) and white (neutral) leads again to confirm that the power is off.

Loosen the clamp holding the power cable to the tank, and pull the power cable free of the tank. You can now proceed to disconnect pipes and cart the old tank away.

Position the new water tank, level it using a carpenter's level and metal shims, and hook up the water pipes.

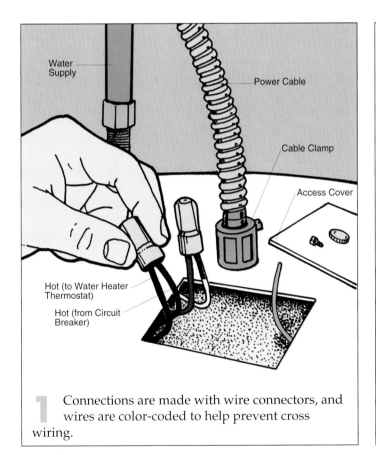

Water Supply

Power Cable

Cable Clamp

Access Cover

Hot (to Water Heater Thermostat)

Hot (from Circuit Breaker)

1 Connections are made with wire connectors, and wires are color-coded to help prevent cross wiring.

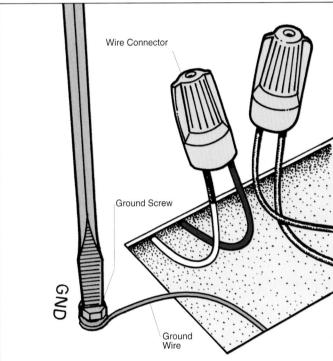

Wire Connector

Ground Screw

GND

Ground Wire

2 Make certain that the ground wire is connected securely to the ground screw, which is identified here by the initials GND.

Remove the cover to open the power cable compartment. Push the power cable into this compartment through the cable clamp that secures the power cable to the tank.

Using wire connectors, connect the hot and neutral wires of the power cable to their respective thermostat wires. Then, loosen the screw marked GRD or GND (for GROUND) and connect the ground wire to it (Figure 2). Be sure you tighten the screw so it grips the ground wire.

Using a screwdriver, tighten the cable clamp and install the cover over the power cable compartment.

Remove the covers over the thermostats and elements. Wearing gloves, pull apart the insulation to reveal the temperature controls.

Turn the temperature control to the desired temperature (Figure 3). Make sure both thermostats are at the same setting; then press the red button on each thermostat (Figure 4). This is an overload reset button. Pressing it will complete the circuit when you turn on the power.

Carefully fold the insulation back over the thermostats, and install both covers. Then install the fuse or turn on the circuit breaker.

After approximately one hour, turn on a hot-water faucet to see whether water is hot. If it isn't, you've done something wrong, so turn off electricity again at the panel and check the connections.

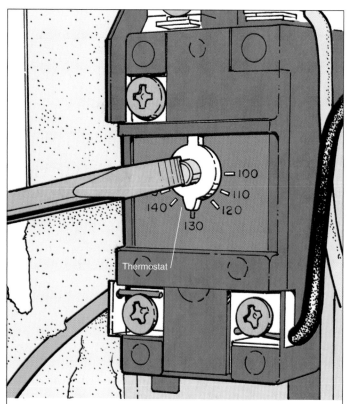

3 Set the temperature to the desired level using a screwdriver. Make sure both thermostats are at the same setting.

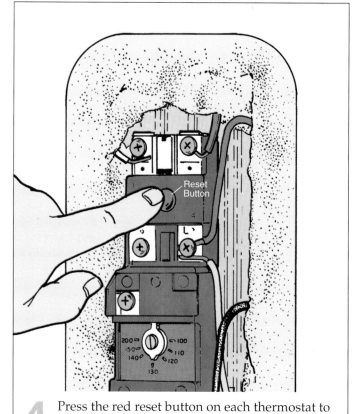

4 Press the red reset button on each thermostat to complete the circuit.

glossary

Adapter A fitting that connects two pipes of different sizes or materials.

Aerator The diverter/screen unit that is screwed onto the end of a faucet to control splashing.

Air chamber A vertical, air-filled pipe that prevents water hammer by absorbing pressure when water is shut off at a faucet.

Air gap Device used in a dishwasher's drainage system that prevents waste water from backing up and contaminating clean water in the dishwasher. Also, the space needed between the source of potable water (a faucet outlet) and the rim of the sink or lavatory it discharges into.

Backflow A reverse flow of water or other liquids into water supply pipes, caused by negative pressure in the pipes.

Backflow preventer A device or means that prevents backflow.

Ballcock A toilet-tank water-supply valve, which is controlled by a float ball.

Branch Any part of a pipe system other than a riser, main, or stack.

Branch bent A vent pipe that runs from a vent stack to a branch drain line.

Caulking A waterproofing compound used to seal plumbing connections.

Cleanout A removable plug in a trap or a drainpipe, which allows easier access for removing blockages inside.

Closet bend A curved drain pipe that is located beneath the base of the toilet.

Closet flange The rim on a closet bend by which that pipe attaches to the floor.

Coupling A fitting used to connect two pipes.

CPVC Chlorinated polyvinyl chloride; a plastic pipe used for hot-water lines.

Diaphragm Used instead of stem washer, this is found on compression faucets.

Diverter valve A device that changes the direction of water flow from one faucet or fixture to another.

Drain Any pipe that carries waste water through a drainage network into the municipal sewer or private septic system.

Drainage network All the piping that carries sewage from a house into the municipal sewer or private septic system.

DWV Drain-waste-vent; the pipe system used to carry away waste.

Elbow A fitting used for making directional changes in pipelines.

Escutcheon A decorative plate that covers the hole in the wall in which the stem or cartridge fits.

Female thread The end of a pipe or fitting with internal threads.

Fitting Any device that joins sections of pipe or connects pipe to a fixture.

Flapper valve A valve that replaces a tank stopper in a toilet.

Float ball The hollow ball on the end of a rod in the toilet tank, which floats upward as the tank fills after flushing and closes the water inlet valve.

Flush valve A device at the bottom of a toilet tank for flushing.

Flux A material applied to the surfaces of copper pipes and fittings to assist in the cleaning and bonding processes.

Gasket A device used to seal joints against leaks.

Hanger A device used to support suspended pipe.

Inlet valve A valve in a toilet tank that controls the flow of water into the tank.

Joint Any connection between pipes, fittings, or other parts of plumbing system.

Lavatory A wash basin located in a bathroom or powder room.

Lift-rod A device that opens and closes pop-up stoppers.

Main Principal water or drain pipe to which all household branches connect.

Main vent (or stack) Principal vent to which branch vents may be connected.

Male threads The end of a fitting, pipe, or fixture connection with external threads.

No-hub (hubless) connector A fitting that connects pipes by means of neoprene sleeves and stainless-steel clamps.

Nominal size The designated dimension of a pipe or fitting; it varies slightly from the actual size.

O-ring A ring of rubber used as a gasket.

Overflow tube A tube in a toilet tank into which water flows if the float arm fails to activate shutoff valve when the tank is filled.

Pipe sleeve A clamp used to patch pipe leaks.

Pipe support Any kind of brace used to support pipe.

Plumber's putty A material used to seal openings around fixtures.

Pop-up valve A device used to open and close drains.

Potable water Water that is safe to drink.

PVC Polyvinyl chloride; a plastic used to make cold-water pipe.

Reducer A fitting used to join two pipes of different diameters.

Relief valve A safety device that automatically releases water due to an excessive buildup of pressure and temperature; used on a water heater.

Riser A water-supply pipe that extends vertically.

Shutoff valve A device set into a water line to allow for interruption of the flow of water to a fixture or appliance.

Soil stack A vertical pipe that carries waste to the sewer drain; also, the vertical main pipe that receives both human and nonhuman waste from a group of fixtures including a toilet or from all plumbing fixtures in a given installation.

Soldering/sweating The process used to join copper pipe.

Stack Any vertical main that is part of the DWV system.

Tap A faucet or hydrant that draws water from a supply line.

Temperature and Pressure relief valve (T & P) Device that prevents temperature and pressure from building up inside the tank and exploding.

T (tee) fitting A pipe fitting that is T-shaped and has three points of connection.

Thermocouple A safety device that automatically turns off gas flowing to the pilot if the flame goes out.

Threaded sweat adapter Used to install cold-water pipes.

Trap The water-filled curved pipe that prevents sewer gas from entering the house through the drainage network.

Tripwaste Lever-controlled bathtub drain stopper; two kinds: pop-up or plunger.

Valve seat The part of the valve into which a washer or other piece fits, stopping the flow of water.

Vent stack A vertical vent pipe.

Waste Discharge from plumbing fixtures or plumbing appliances.

Water drain cock A device that allows the water-heater tank to be drained.

Water hammer A knocking in water pipes caused by a sudden change in pressure after a faucet or water valve shuts off.

Wax ring A wax seal used to seal the base of a toilet so it will not leak.

Y (wye) fitting A fitting used in drainage systems for connecting branch lines to horizontal drainage lines; also provides cleanouts.

index